Letts

CW00801285

GCSE

VISUAL
REVISION
GUIDE

SUCCESS

QUESTIONS & ANSWERS

& ANSWERS

CHEMISTRY

● MULTIPLE CHOICE ● QUICK TESTS ● MOCK GCSE QUESTIONS

Top ten tips for using the **GCSE Questions and Answers series** for successful revision.

1. The Visual Revision Question and Answer books are the vibrant and fun way to aid active revision.

2. Each topic relates to pages in your Visual Revision Success Guide, so use the Questions and Answers to test how well you have revised the topic.

3. Section A questions are warm-up multiple choice questions to get your brain cells ticking.

4. Section B questions put revision into practice with quiz-style short-answer questions.

5. Section C questions show you the kind of thing you can expect to find in a **GCSE** paper – these will give you heaps of practice for those all-important exams.

6. At the end of each topic, add up the total marks you have scored and enter them in the Homework Diary.

7. Don't worry if you score low in a section – just re-read the information in your Success Guide and try again!

8. Do not try to plough through the book in one go – remember the little and often rule. Short bursts of about 30 minutes, followed by a break, work best.

9. Get used to the style of questions used in the exams. Highlight the key words in the question, plan your response and ensure that your answer is relevant.

10. In the exam ... Follow all instructions in the exam paper. Read the questions very carefully. Check the number of marks available for each question and answer accordingly. Keep an eye on the time – make sure you answer the correct number of questions and leave time to read through your answers.

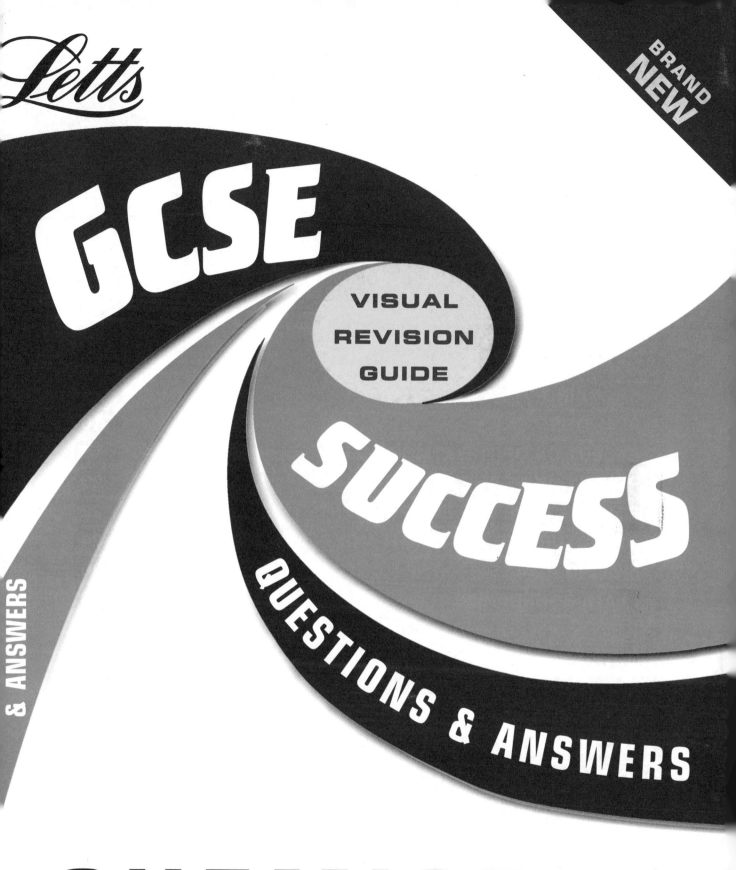

Letts

BRAND NEW

GCSE

VISUAL
REVISION
GUIDE

SUCCESS

QUESTIONS & ANSWERS

& ANSWERS

CHEMISTRY

Author

Emma Poole

CONTENTS

HOMEWORK DIARY

TOPIC	SCORE
Limestone	/23
Rocks	/16
Clues in Rocks	/23
Fossil Fuels	/22
Cracking	/19
Plastics	/19
Evolution of the Atmosphere	/20
Pollution of the Atmosphere	/21
Pollution of the Environment	/19
Structure of the Earth and Plate Tectonics	/23
Moving Plates	/19
Plate Boundaries	/22
Metals	/20
Reactivity Series	/19
Metal Displacement Reactions	/22
Extraction of Iron	/30
Purification of Copper and Extraction of Aluminium	/25
Acids and Alkalis	/21
Making Salts	/31
States of Matter	/16
Atomic Structure	/30
Ionic and Covalent Bonding	/13
Ionic and Covalent Compounds	/16
The Periodic Table	/17
Transition Metals	/23
Group I – The Alkali Metals	/24
Group VII – The Halogens	/22
The Noble Gases	/19
Electrolysis of Brine	/23
Common Tests and Safety Hazards	/20
Rates of Reaction	/18
Catalysts and Enzymes	/21
Exothermic and Endothermic Reactions	/14
Reversible Reactions	/18
The Haber Process	/18
Relative Formula Mass	/22
Relative Formula Mass II	/24
Balancing Equations	/24
Calculating Masses	/21
Electrolysis	/21
Types of Reaction	/15

EXAM HINTS

- Make sure you read <u>all of</u> the question <u>very carefully</u>. If a question includes a <u>diagram</u> look at this too. If you rush you may miss some <u>important pieces of information</u>.

- Look at the <u>number of marks available</u> for each question. Use the number of marks as a guide as to <u>how much you should write for your answer</u>.

- Some questions involve <u>calculations</u>. Always show your <u>working</u> and include units if they are required.

- Don't worry if a question appears to be <u>on a subject you have not covered</u> during your chemistry lessons. These questions are designed to see how you can use <u>new information</u>.

- Some questions require <u>extended writing</u>. Make sure you <u>plan your answer</u> so that you make all the points you want to and <u>do not repeat yourself</u>.

- Some questions involve writing <u>chemical symbols</u>. Remember if a symbol has two letters the <u>first one must be a capital</u> and the <u>second must be lower case</u>.

- If you need to write the <u>formula</u> for a substance make sure you write it <u>accurately</u>.

- Make sure you can recognise the pieces of <u>science equipment</u> (described in words or diagrams) which may be referred to in questions.

- If you are asked to name a substance <u>give the name and not the formula</u>.

- If you are asked to write a <u>formula equation</u> make sure that your <u>equation balances</u>.

EARTH MATERIALS

LIMESTONE

A Choose just one answer, a, b, c or d.

1 What type of rock is limestone?
(a) sedimentary   (c) igneous
(b) metamorphic   (d) mineral   (1 mark)

2 What type of reaction occurs when calcium carbonate is heated?
(a) thermal decomposition
(b) exothermic
(c) neutralisation
(d) displacement   (1 mark)

3 The gas given off when calcium carbonate is heated is
(a) carbon monoxide
(b) oxygen
(c) nitrogen
(d) carbon dioxide   (1 mark)

4 Heating a mixture of limestone, sand and soda produces a useful new substance. What is this substance called?
(a) concrete
(b) cement
(c) glass
(d) quicklime   (1 mark)

5 Roasting powdered clay with powdered limestone produces
(a) concrete
(b) cement
(c) glass
(d) quicklime   (1 mark)

Score   /5

B Answer all parts of the questions.

1 Complete the following word equations.

(a) calcium carbonate → calcium oxide + ...

(b) calcium oxide + water → ....

Complete the following symbol equations.

(c) $CaCO_3$ → .... + CO_2

(d) $CaO + H_2O$ → ....   (4 marks)

2 Consider the following sentences. Decide whether each one is true or false.

(a) Powdered limestone can neutralise the acidity in lakes caused by acid rain.

(b) The main compound in limestone is calcium oxide.

(c) Concrete is strong but very expensive to produce.

(d) Slaked lime will neutralise the acidity in soils faster than powdered limestone.

(e) When calcium oxide is reacted with water, the product is calcium carbonate.   (5 marks)

Score   /9

C These are GCSE-style questions. Answer all parts of the questions.

1 Complete the table below to show the use of each of these substances:

glass   limestone   quicklime   limewater

Substance	Use
a)	Can be cut into blocks and used in building
b)	Can be used to make windows and windscreens
c)	Can be spread on fields to reduce the acidity of soils
d)	Can be used to test for the gas carbon dioxide

(4 marks)

2 Limestone can be heated to make quicklime. Quicklime can be reacted with water to form slaked lime.

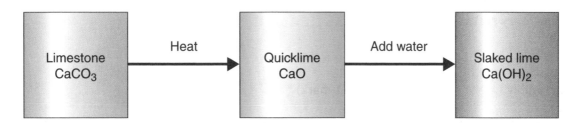

Limestone $CaCO_3$ → Heat →   Quicklime CaO → Add water →   Slaked lime $Ca(OH)_2$

(a) What is the name of the reaction in which limestone is broken down to form calcium oxide? Circle one answer. (1 mark)

combustion   thermal decomposition   electrolysis   neutralisation

(b) This reaction can be represented by a word equation.

Calcium carbonate → calcium oxide + carbon dioxide

The reaction can also be represented by a symbol equation. Complete the symbol equation below to show the reaction. (2 marks)

$CaCO_3$ → .... + ...

3 Limestone can also be made into glass. Glass is a very useful substance. Explain how limestone can be made into glass.

....

.... (2 marks)

Score   /9

How well did you do?
1–7   Try again
8–12   Getting there
13–18   Good work
19–23   Excellent!

TOTAL SCORE   /23

For more on this topic
see page 4 of your Success Guide

7

ROCKS

A Choose just one answer, a, b, c or d.

1 To which type of rock does granite belong?
(a) sedimentary
(b) metamorphic
(c) extrusive igneous
(d) intrusive igneous   (1 mark)

2 To which type of rock does basalt belong?
(a) sedimentary
(b) metamorphic
(c) extrusive igneous
(d) intrusive igneous   (1 mark)

3 Sedimentary rocks tend to be
(a) hard
(b) shiny
(c) black
(d) crumbly   (1 mark)

4 Which type of rock may contain fossils?
(a) sedimentary
(b) metamorphic
(c) extrusive igneous
(d) intrusive igneous   (1 mark)

5 How can metamorphic rocks be formed?
(a) from sediments
(b) by high temperature and pressure
(c) only by high temperatures
(d) only by high pressures   (1 mark)

Score   /5

B Answer all parts of the questions.

1 Connect the name of each rock type to its description and to the type of rock it belongs to.   (3 marks)

Name | Description | Rock type

biotite schist

rounded pebbles of quartz and flint in a matrix of much finer grains of silt and sand

igneous

syenite

coarse-grained interlocking pink, grey and white crystals

sedimentary

conglomerate

folded bands of black and brown crystals

metamorphic

2 What is a fossil? .... (1 mark)

Score   /4

C These are GCSE-style questions. Answer all parts of the questions.

1 The cross-section below shows the different rocks that were found in a cliff face. X represents part of a large igneous intrusion and Y represents a smaller igneous intrusion called a sill.

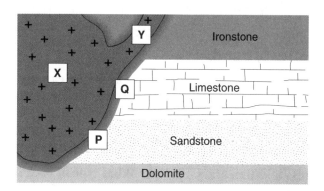

Both the rocks found at X and at Y contain crystals.

(a) Where are the larger crystals found?

.... (1 mark)

(b) Explain why the crystals are larger at the site you have chosen.

.... (1 mark)

(c) What type of rock is limestone?

.... (1 mark)

(d) What type of rock is formed around the outside of the igneous intrusions X and Y?

.... (1 mark)

(e) Why is the rock formed at Q different to the rock formed at P?

.... (1 mark)

(f) The rock at Q was originally limestone. What is the name of the rock that it has formed?

.... (1 mark)

2 Place these events in order to show the story of how this cliff face was formed. Place the earliest event first. (1 mark)

(a) Limestone is deposited.   **(d)** Dolomite is deposited.

(b) Igneous rock is intruded.   **(e)** Ironstone is deposited.

(c) Sandstone is deposited.

Score   /7

How well did you do?

1–5 Try again
6–10 Getting there
11–13 Good work
14–16 Excellent!

TOTAL SCORE   /16

For more on this topic
see page 6 of your Success Guide

CLUES IN ROCKS

Choose just one answer, a, b, c or d.

1 Mudstone is an example of which type of rock?
  (a) metamorphic
  (b) sedimentary
  (c) extrusive igneous
  (d) intrusive igneous (1 mark)

2 An igneous rock cuts across a sedimentary rock. What can be said about the rocks?
  (a) The igneous rock must be older than the sedimentary rock.
  (b) The igneous rock must be basalt.
  (c) The sedimentary rock is older than the igneous rock.
  (d) Older sedimentary rock is probably found above younger sedimentary rock. (1 mark)

3 A geologist can use ripple marks to tell
  (a) which way up the rock formed
  (b) the date the rock was formed
  (c) the time until the next earthquake
  (d) the distance to the nearest volcano (1 mark)

4 What type of rock is slate?
  (a) metamorphic
  (b) sedimentary
  (c) intrusive igneous
  (d) extrusive igneous (1 mark)

5 What type of rock is basalt?
  (a) metamorphic
  (b) sedimentary
  (c) intrusive igneous
  (d) extrusive igneous (1 mark)

Score /5

B **Answer all parts of the questions.**

1 The diagram below shows the rocks in a cliff face. Place the rocks in age order.

Newest rock...

....

....

....

Oldest rock .... (5 marks)

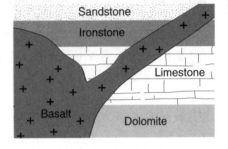
Sandstone
Ironstone
Limestone
Basalt
Dolomite

2 Complete the following passage.

Layers of rock may be stressed due to large

.... in the Earth's crust.

If rock layers become bent, a

.... is formed. Sometimes

the rock can be subjected to such a big force that the rock snaps.

This is known as a ....

(3 marks)

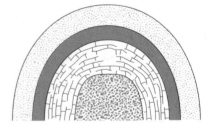

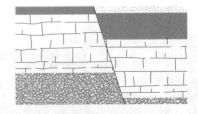

Score /8

C **These are GCSE-style questions. Answer all parts of the questions.**

1 The cross-section below shows the different rocks that were found in a cliff face.

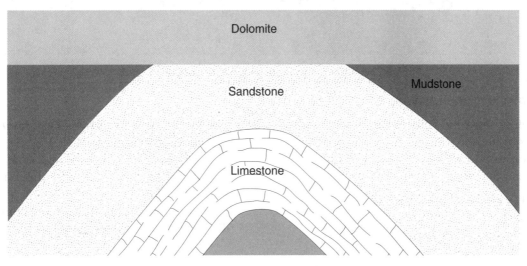

Place these events below in order to show how the rock face was formed.
Put the earliest event first.

Dolomite is deposited.   Mudstone is deposited.

Rocks are weathered.   Rocks are folded.

Limestone is deposited.   Sandstone is deposited.

....

....

.... (6 marks)

2 Rocks are continually being broken down and then reformed into new rocks.
The diagrams show three cross-sections of rock that has been changed.
Label each of the rock cross-sections with a description from the list below.

| tilted | folded | faulted | weathered |

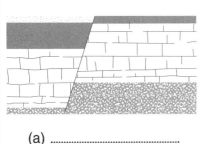      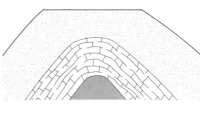

(a) ....   (b) ....   (c) .... and

then ....

(4 marks)

Score   /10

How well did you do?
1–7   Try again
8–12   Getting there
13–18 Good work
19–23 Excellent!

TOTAL SCORE   /23

For more on this topic
see page 8 of your Success Guide

11

FOSSIL FUELS

A

Choose just one answer, a, b, c or d.

1 Which of these substances could be classified as fossil fuels?
(a) coal and uranium
(c) wave and coal
(b) solar and wind
(d) coal and oil (1 mark)

2 What is crude oil a mixture of?
(a) plastics
(b) elements
(c) hydrocarbons
(d) solids (1 mark)

3 Which of these descriptions best describes a short chain hydrocarbon?
(a) runny, hard to ignite and high boiling point
(b) viscous, hard to ignite and high boiling point
(c) viscous, easy to ignite and low boiling point
(d) runny, easy to ignite and low boiling point (1 mark)

4 Which of these descriptions best describes a long chain hydrocarbon?
(a) runny, hard to ignite and high boiling point
(b) viscous, hard to ignite and high boiling point (1 mark)
(c) viscous, easy to ignite and low boiling point
(d) runny, hard to ignite and low boiling point (1 mark)

5 Fossil fuels can best be described as being
(a) volcanic
(b) renewable
(c) non-renewable
(d) illegal (1 mark)

Score   /5

B

Answer all parts of the questions.

1 Place these events in chronological (oldest event first) order to show how the fossil fuel coal can be formed.

(a) The dead plants and animals were covered by sediment.

(b) After millions of years, coal was formed.

(c) Plants and animals died and fell to the swamp floor.

(d) The plants and animals in the absence of oxygen did not decay.

(e) As the layers of sediment built up, the remains became heated and pressurised. (5 marks)

2 True or false?

	True	False
(a) Crude oil is a mixture of hydrocarbons.	☐	☐
(b) Hydrocarbons contain the elements carbon, hydrogen and oxygen.	☐	☐
(c) A molecule of the hydrocarbon petrol contains about 15 carbon atoms.	☐	☐
(d) Fractional distillation can be used to separate a mixture of hydrocarbons.	☐	☐
(e) Long chain hydrocarbons are useful as fuels.	☐	☐

(5 marks)

Score   /10

C

These are GCSE-style questions. Answer all parts of the questions.

1 Crude oil is a mixture of different hydrocarbons.
Crude oil can be separated into a number of fractions.

(a) Name the two elements found in hydrocarbons.

.... (2 marks)

(b) What is the name given to this process used to separate crude oil into different fractions?

Circle one answer.

filtration   chromatography

fractional distillation   crystallisation   (1 mark)

(c) Which of the hydrocarbon fractions shown in the diagram opposite has the smallest molecules?

.... (1 mark)

(d) Which of the hydrocarbon fractions shown in the diagram would be easiest to ignite?

.... (1 mark)

(e) Which of the hydrocarbon fractions shown in the diagram would be the most viscous?

.... (1 mark)

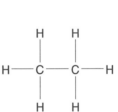

Refinery gas

Petrol

Naphtha

Kerosene

Diesel

Oil

Crude oil

Bitumen

2 Which of the hydrocarbon molecules below would have the highest boiling point? Circle one answer.

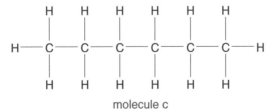

molecule a   molecule b

molecule c

(1 mark)

Score   /7

How well did you do?

1–7   Try again
8–12   Getting there
13–18   Good work
19–22   Excellent!

TOTAL SCORE   /22

For more on this topic
see page 10 of your Success Guide

CRACKING

Choose just one answer, a, b, c or d.

1 What are saturated hydrocarbons called?
(a) alkenes   (c) alkynes
(b) viscous   (d) alkanes   (1 mark)

2 A compound has the formula C_2H_6. What is it called?
(a) ethane
(b) methane
(c) ethene
(d) propene   (1 mark)

3 Alkenes react with bromine water. The colour change is
(a) colourless to orange/brown
(b) blue to red/orange
(c) colourless to purple
(d) orange/brown to colourless   (1 mark)

4 The alkane family of hydrocarbons
(a) have carbon–carbon double bonds
(b) are saturated hydrocarbons
(c) react with bromine water
(d) contain several ionic bonds   (1 mark)

5 What is the name of the catalyst used to crack hydrocarbons?
(a) platinum
(b) copper sulphate
(c) hydrogen peroxide
(d) hot aluminium oxide   (1 mark)

Score   /5

Answer all parts of the question.

1 (a) Name these hydrocarbons.

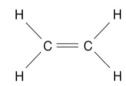

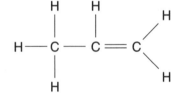

(i) ....

(ii) ....

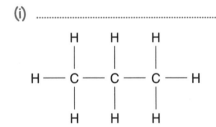

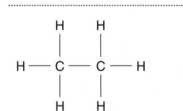

(iii) ....

(iv) ....   (4 marks)

(b) Which of these hydrocarbons belong to the alkane family? ....

(c) Which of these hydrocarbons could be described as unsaturated? ....

(d) Which of these hydrocarbons would react with bromine water? ....

(e) Describe the colour change that would be observed when bromine water reacts with an alkene.

....   (4 marks)

Score   /8

C These are GCSE-style questions. Answer all parts of the questions.

1 (a) Crude oil is a mixture of hydrocarbons. What is the name given to the technique used to separate crude oil into different fractions?

.... (1 mark)

(b) Large hydrocarbon molecules are less useful than smaller hydrocarbon molecules. What is the name given to the process in which larger hydrocarbon molecules are broken down into smaller hydrocarbons?

.... (1 mark)

2 The diagrams below show the structural formulae of three hydrocarbons.

Molecule a

Molecule b

Molecule c

(a) Which of these hydrocarbon molecules is an alkene?

.... (1 mark)

(b) What is the name of hydrocarbon molecule b?

.... (1 mark)

(c) Which of these hydrocarbon molecules could be found in petrol?

.... (1 mark)

(d) Which of these hydrocarbon molecules could be used to make the polymer polythene?

.... (1 mark)

Score   /6

How well did you do?

1–5   Try again
6–11   Getting there
12–15 Good work
16–19 Excellent!

TOTAL SCORE   /19

For more on this topic
see page **12** of your Success Guide

15

PLASTICS

A **Choose just one answer, a, b, c or d.**

1 What are plastic bags made from?
(a) paper
(b) PVC
(c) polypropene
(d) polythene   (1 mark)

2 What are plastic drain pipes made from?
(a) aluminium
(b) PVC
(c) polypropene
(d) polythene   (1 mark)

3 By what type of reaction can ethene molecules be made into polythene?
(a) addition polymerisation
(b) substitution
(c) condensation polymerisation
(d) displacement   (1 mark)

4 Which of these sentences best describes the plastic, polypropene?
(a) strong and highly elastic
(b) cheap and strong
(c) rigid and cheap
(d) cheap and can be moulded   (1 mark)

5 Polypropene is made from many small monomer molecules. Which of these monomers could be made into polypropene?
(a) propene
(b) ethane
(c) propane
(d) ethane   (1 mark)

Score   /5

B **Answer all parts of the questions.**

1 True or false?   True   False

(a) Ethane is a monomer that can be made into polyethene. ☐ ☐

(b) 'Poly' means three. ☐ ☐

(c) PVC is useful because it is very flexible. ☐ ☐

(d) Ethene is made into polythene by heating many ethene molecules with a catalyst under high pressure. ☐ ☐

(e) The monomers used to make plastics contain double bonds. ☐ ☐   (5 marks)

2 Draw diagrams to show the polymers formed from each of these monomers.   (4 marks)

(a)

$$H_2C=CH_2 + H_2C=CH_2 + H_2C=CH_2 \longrightarrow$$

(b)

$$CH_2=CH(CH_3) + CH_2=CH(CH_3) + CH_2=CH(CH_3) \longrightarrow$$

Score   /9

C These are GCSE-style questions. Answer all parts of the questions.

1 (a) Which of these structural formulae represents the polymer, polythene?

.... (1 mark)

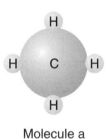

Compound a

Compound c

Compound b

Compound d

(b) Give one use of the plastic, polythene.

.... (1 mark)

2 The diagrams below show three different hydrocarbons.

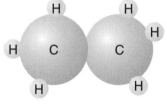

Molecule a

Molecule b

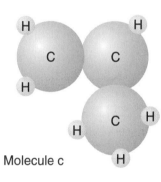

Molecule c

(a) Which of these diagrams represents an unsaturated hydrocarbon?

.... (1 mark)

(b) What is the name of 'molecule a'?

.... (1 mark)

(c) Lots of molecules of 'molecule c' could be joined together to form a polymer. What is the name of this polymer?

.... (1 mark)

Score   /5

How well did you do?

1–5	Start again
6–11	Getting there
12–15	Good work
16–19	Excellent!

TOTAL SCORE   /19

For more on this topic
see page **14** of your Success Guide

EVOLUTION OF THE ATMOSPHERE

A

Choose just one answer, a, b, c or d.

1 Which gases comprised the Earth's early atmosphere?
(a) carbon dioxide, steam, ammonia and methane
(b) oxygen, nitrogen and trace amounts of carbon dioxide, water vapour and noble gases
(c) carbon monoxide and water vapour
(d) oxygen, nitrogen and carbon monoxide
(1 mark)

2 For how long have levels of carbon dioxide in the atmosphere been rising?
(a) since the last general election
(b) the last 200 years (since the Industrial Revolution)
(c) since the Middle Ages
(d) the last 20 years
(1 mark)

3 How is the extra carbon dioxide in the atmosphere produced?
(a) when fossil fuels are formed
(b) when fossil fuels are burnt
(c) when fossil fuels are mined
(d) when fossil fuels are buried
(1 mark)

4 Which gases comprise the Earth's atmosphere today?
(a) carbon dioxide, steam, ammonia and methane
(b) nitrogen, oxygen and trace amounts of carbon dioxide, water vapour and noble gases
(c) carbon monoxide and water vapour
(d) oxygen, nitrogen and carbon monoxide
(1 mark)

5 Why is the ozone layer useful to us?
(a) It stops acid rain.
(b) It prevents global warming.
(c) It filters out harmful UV rays.
(d) It helps reduce car crime.
(1 mark)

Score /5

B

Answer all parts of the questions.

1 Place these events in order to show how the Earth's atmosphere has evolved.

(a) Plants evolved and soon colonised most of the Earth.

(b) Carbon dioxide became locked up as carbonate minerals and in fossil fuels.

(c) Enormous volcanic activity produced carbon dioxide, steam, ammonia and methane.

(d) Plants removed carbon dioxide and produced oxygen.

(e) The water vapour (steam) condensed to form the early oceans.
(7 marks)

2 Explain how much of the carbon dioxide produced by burning fossil fuels is removed from

the atmosphere. ....

....

....
(2 marks)

Score /9

C **This is a GCSE-style question. Answer all parts of the question.**

1 **(a)** Complete the pie diagram with the labels below to show the composition of the Earth's atmosphere today.

| Oxygen | Nitrogen | Other gases |

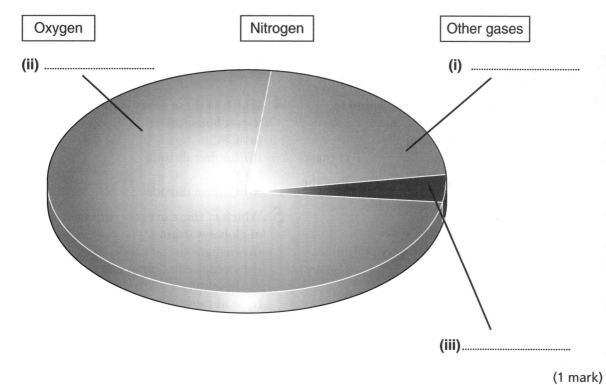

(ii) ....

(i) ....

(iii) ....

(1 mark)

(b) The Earth's early atmosphere was mainly carbon dioxide, with very little oxygen. Give the name of one other gas found in the Earth's early atmosphere.

.... (1 mark)

(c) Explain how the Earth's early atmosphere was formed.

.... (1 mark)

(d) Over time, the amount of carbon dioxide decreased and the amount of oxygen increased. Why did this happen?

.... (1 mark)

(e) What protects the Earth by filtering harmful UV rays?

.... (1 mark)

(f) Most of the carbon from the carbon dioxide in the Earth's early atmosphere is now found in sedimentary rocks. Some of the carbon is found in fossil fuels. In which other type of rock is the carbon found?

Tick one answer.

Sandstone ☐   Carbonate ☐   Granite ☐   Basalt ☐   (1 mark)

Score   /6

How well did you do?

1–5   Try again
6–11   Getting there
12–15 Good work
16–20 Excellent!

TOTAL SCORE   /20

For more on this topic
see page 16 of your Success Guide

POLLUTION OF THE ATMOSPHERE

A Choose just one answer, a, b, c or d.

1 Which of these elements may be found in fossil fuels?
(a) coal   (c) silicon
(b) sulphur   (d) tin   (1 mark)

2 Which of these descriptions best describes the gas carbon monoxide?
(a) green and dense
(b) colourless can be smelt
(c) colourless, odourless and very poisonous
(d) poisonous and violet   (1 mark)

3 Historically, which of these uses have **not** involved CFCs?
(a) aerosols
(b) fridges
(c) solvents
(d) roll-on deodorants   (1 mark)

4 Which of these gases is linked with the 'Greenhouse effect'?
(a) CFCs
(b) sulphur dioxide
(c) Water
(d) Carbon dioxide   (1 mark)

5 Which of these events could be a consequence of global warming?
(a) changes to the ozone layer
(b) icecaps could melt and cause massive flooding
(c) acid rain
(d) faulty gas appliances   (1 mark)

Score   /5

B Answer all parts of the questions.

1 Match each environmental problem to the chemical responsible for it and to one possible consequence.
(6 marks)

Environmental problem	Chemical responsible	Possible consequences
Greenhouse effect	Sulphur dioxide	Damage to lakes, trees and buildings
The hole in the ozone layer	Carbon dioxide	Ice caps melt causing massive flooding
Acid rain	CFCs	Skin cancers in animals and damage to crops

2 Explain how carbon dioxide may cause global warming.

....

....

.... (2 marks)

3 Explain how sulphur dioxide is linked to fossil fuels.

....

.... (2 marks)

Score   /10

C This is a GCSE-style question. Answer all parts of the question.

1 Humans are affecting the proportion of gases in the atmosphere.

(a) Explain how and why the level of carbon dioxide in the atmosphere is changing.

....

.... (1 mark)

(b) Explain how acid rain is produced.

....

.... (1 mark)

(c) Which of these environmental problems could be caused by acid rain?

Tick two boxes.

damage to statues ☐   skin cancers ☐

damage to trees ☐   changes to weather patterns ☐ (1 mark)

(d) CFCs are very stable compounds that were widely used in aerosols. Which of these environmental problems is associated with CFCs?

Circle one answer.

     Greenhouse effect

     Acid rain

     Holes in the ozone layer (1 mark)

2 (a) Which of these environmental problems could be caused by increasing levels of carbon dioxide in the atmosphere?

Circle one answer.

     Greenhouse effect

     Acid rain

     Holes in the ozone layer (1 mark)

(b) Give one possible consequence of a small increase in the level of carbon dioxide in the atmosphere.

....

.... (1 mark)

Score   /6

How well did you do?

1–5   Try again
6–11   Getting there
12–15   Good work
16–21   Excellent!

TOTAL SCORE   /21

For more on this topic
see page 18 of your Success Guide

POLLUTION OF THE ENVIRONMENT

A Choose just one answer, a, b, c or d.

1 Which of these gases can be produced when PVC is burnt?
(a) hydrogen chloride   (c) bromine
(b) iodine   (d) phosphorus
(1 mark)

2 Which of these substances could be described as non-biodegradable?
(a) bananas   (c) plastics
(b) leaves   (d) newspapers
(1 mark)

3 Which of these issues could be an advantage of limestone quarrying in an area?
(a) destruction of animal habitats
(b) new jobs and money
(c) scarring of the landscape
(d) many heavy lorries
(1 mark)

4 Which of these statements is true of non-biodegradable plastics?
(a) They are reactive.
(b) They do not rot away.
(c) They react with water.
(d) They react with the oxygen in air. (1 mark)

5 Which of these substances can cause eutrophication in lakes?
(a) carbon dioxide
(b) limestone
(c) nitrate fertilisers
(d) oil
(1 mark)

Score /5

B Answer all parts of the question.

1 (a) Nitrate fertilisers can cause environmental problems. Place the events below in order to show how such a problem can occur. (5 marks)

(i) Algae grow extremely well.

(ii) The bacteria use up all the oxygen in the water.

(iii) Nitrate fertilisers used by farmers are washed into streams and lakes.

(iv) Fish and other animals cannot get enough oxygen and die.

(v) The algae die and bacteria start to break down (decompose) the algae.

(b) What is the name given to this problem? (1 mark)

....

(c) What other problems have been linked to nitrate fertilisers?

.... (2 marks)

Score /8

C This is a GCSE-style question. Answer all parts of the question.

1 A small village is located near to a large area of limestone.

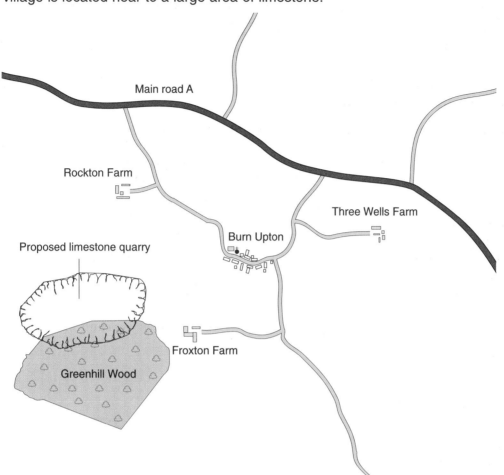

(a) What type of rock is limestone?

.... (1 mark)

(b) Limestone is an important raw material. Give a use of limestone.

.... (1 mark)

(c) Discuss the advantages and disadvantages of building a quarry at this site.

....

....

....

....

....

.... (4 marks)

Score   /6

How well did you do?
1–5   Try again
6–11   Getting there
12–15   Good work
16–19   Excellent!

TOTAL SCORE   /19

For more on this topic
see page 20 of your Success Guide

23

STRUCTURE OF THE EARTH AND PLATE TECTONICS

A Choose just one answer, a, b, c or d.

1 Which of these layers is found at the centre of the Earth?
(a) outer core   (c) crust
(b) inner core   (d) mantle   (1 mark)

2 Where does our knowledge of the layered structure of the Earth come from?
(a) drilling holes
(b) drilling ice cores
(c) studies of the moon
(d) examination of the pathways of seismic waves   (1 mark)

3 What does the Earth's lithosphere comprise?
(a) mantle and outer core
(b) inner and outer core
(c) crust and upper mantle
(d) crust, mantle and outer core   (1 mark)

4 What is believed to cause the convection currents that drive the movement of the Earth's plates?
(a) earthquakes
(b) Icelandic power stations
(c) natural radioactive decay
(d) magnetism   (1 mark)

5 At what rate do the Earth's plates move?
(a) the speed of sound
(b) about as fast as your finger nails grow
(c) as fast as you can walk
(d) as fast as you can run   (1 mark)

Score   /5

B Answer all parts of the questions.

1 Label the diagram below to show the layered structure of the Earth.

(a) _____

(b) _____

(c) _____

(d) _____

(e) _____

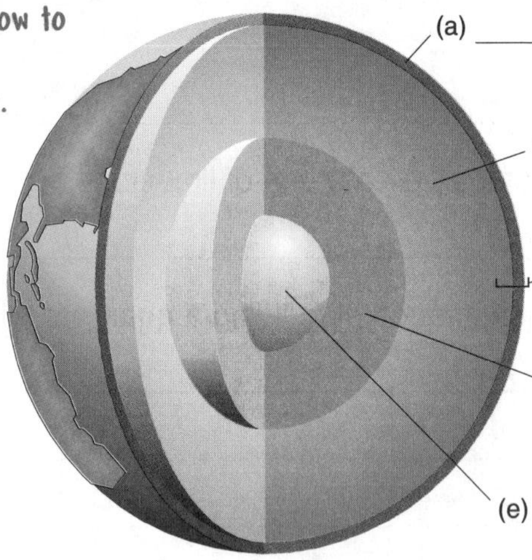

(5 marks)

2 True or false?

	True	False
(a) At one time, the continents were joined together to form one super continent called Pangea.	☐	☐
(b) The Earth's lithosphere is split into three plates.	☐	☐
(c) We believe that the core of the Earth is made of iron and platinum.	☐	☐
(d) Oceanic crust is mainly made of basalt.	☐	☐
(e) The outer core of the Earth is liquid, while the inner core is solid due to the high pressure that it is under.	☐	☐

(5 marks)

Score   /10

C This is a GCSE-style question. Answer all parts of the question.

1 **(a)** The diagram shows a cross-section through the Earth. Complete the diagram by naming each of the layers using the labels below.

| inner core | outer core | crust | mantle |

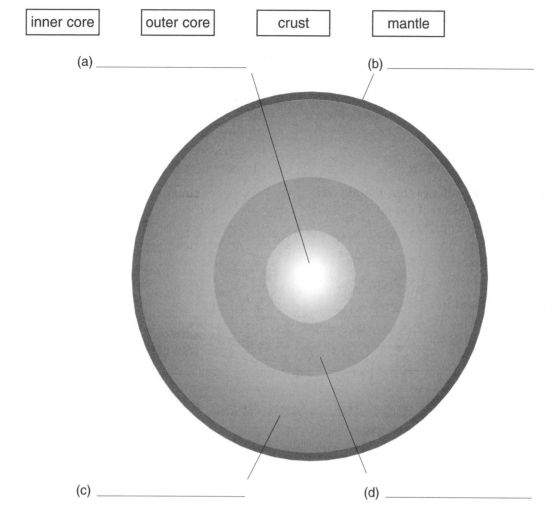

(a) _____   (b) _____

(c) _____   (d) _____   (4 marks)

(b) What is the name given to the crust and the top part of the mantle?

.... (1 mark)

(c) The Earth's core can be split into two parts, the inner core and the outer core.

    (i) What do we believe that the Earth's core is made from?

.... (1 mark)

    (ii) In which state is the material in the Earth's outer core?

.... (1 mark)

    (iii) In which state is the material in the Earth's inner core?

.... (1 mark)

Score   /8

How well did you do?

1–7   Try again
8–12   Getting there
13–18   Good work
19–23   Excellent!

TOTAL SCORE   /23

For more on this topic
see page 22 of your Success Guide

25

MOVING PLATES

A **Choose just one answer, a, b, c or d.**

1 When South America was first mapped, with which continents coast did it appear to form a jigsaw fit?
(a) Europe   (c) Asia
(b) Australia   (d) Africa   (1 mark)

2 British rocks show evidence that Britain has experienced which different climatic zones?
(a) tropical swamps and deserts
(b) polar and desert
(c) tropical swamp and polar
(d) equatorial and polar   (1 mark)

3 Which element found in basalt is magnetic?
(a) magnesium   (c) iron
(b) aluminium   (d) calcium   (1 mark)

4 What type of rock is basalt?
(a) sedimentary
(b) intrusive igneous
(c) extrusive igneous
(d) metamorphic   (1 mark)

5 Where are constructive plate boundaries most often found?
(a) under oceans
(b) in America
(c) on land
(d) in Britain   (1 mark)

Score   /5

B **Answer all parts of the questions.**

1 The basalt rocks on either side of a mid-ocean ridge show a striped magnetic reversal pattern. Place the statements below in order to show how these rocks are formed.

(a) As the new basalt forms, the iron in the iron rich minerals lines up in the opposite direction.

(b) Roughly every half a million years the Earth's magnetic field reverses.

(c) Magma comes to the surface.

(d) As the basalt forms, the iron in the iron-rich minerals lines up with the Earth's magnetic field.

(e) The magma solidifies to form the rock basalt, which is rich in iron.   (5 marks)

2 Give three pieces of evidence that suggest that the theory of plate tectonics is correct.

....

....

....   (3 marks)

Score   /8

C These are GCSE-style questions. Answer all parts of the questions.

1 The Earth's lithosphere is split into about twelve plates. Scientists believe that these plates are slowly moving. The diagram below shows South America and Africa. It is thought that South America and Africa were once joined together.

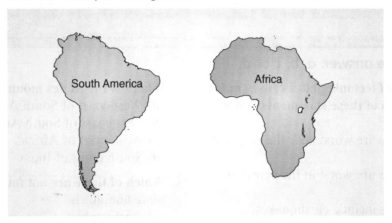

(a) What is the Earth's lithosphere?

.... (1 mark)

(b) Give two pieces of evidence that suggest that South America and Africa could once have been joined together.

....

.... (2 marks)

2 The diagram shows the magnetic reversal pattern of rocks below the Atlantic Ocean. The black stripes show reversed magnetised crust, while the white stripes show normally magnetic crust.

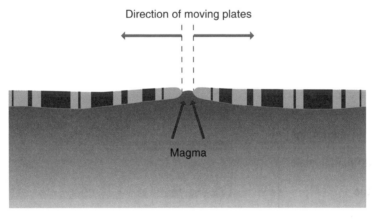

Explain how this magnetic reversal pattern of the rocks at ocean ridges supports the theory of plate tectonics.

....

.... (3 marks)

Score   /6

How well did you do?
1–5 Try again
6–10 Getting there
11–13 Good work
14–19 Excellent!

TOTAL SCORE   /19

For more on this topic
see page 24 of your Success Guide

PLATE BOUNDARIES

A **Choose just one answer, a, b, c or d.**

1 The movement of tectonic plates causes many problems. Which of these statements is not true?
(a) The problems are worst near the edges of plates.
(b) The problems are worst in the centre of plates.
(c) The problems include earthquakes.
(d) The problems include volcanoes.   (1 mark)

2 Where is the San Andreas Fault?
(a) Kansas
(b) Florida
(c) California
(d) Arizona   (1 mark)

3 Where is the Andes mountain range?
(a) West coast of South America
(b) East coast of South America
(c) West coast of Africa
(d) South coast of India   (1 mark)

4 Which of these are not found naturally at plate boundaries?
(a) earthquakes   (c) volcanoes
(b) mountain belts   (d) reservoirs   (1 mark)

5 What happens at a convergent plate boundary?
(a) Plates move apart.
(b) Plates collide.
(c) Plates slide past each other.
(d) Continental plate is forced beneath oceanic plate.   (1 mark)

Score   /5

B **Answer all parts of the questions.**

1 Label the diagram below to show what can happen at a convergent plate boundary between an oceanic and a continental plate.

Use the labels shown in the box.

melting   fold mountains
oceanic plate continental plate
volcano

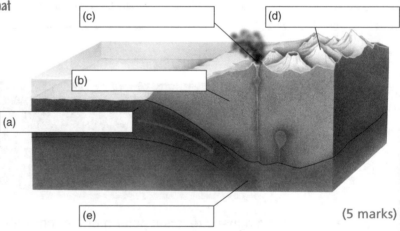

(c) ____ (d) ____ (b) ____ (a) ____ (e) ____   (5 marks)

2 Complete the following passage.

Earthquakes are often found along plate _____ . They occur when the plates _____ past each other. A famous earthquake zone is along the _____ Fault in California. The _____ in this area have been broken into a complicated pattern. As the plates slip past each other they often get _____ together. The _____ on the plates gradually build up, until eventually the plates move and the strain is released as an _____. (7 marks)

Score   /12

C This is a GCSE-style question. Answer all parts of the question.

1 The Earth's lithosphere is split into a number of moving plates. The diagram shows an oceanic and a continental plate moving towards each other.

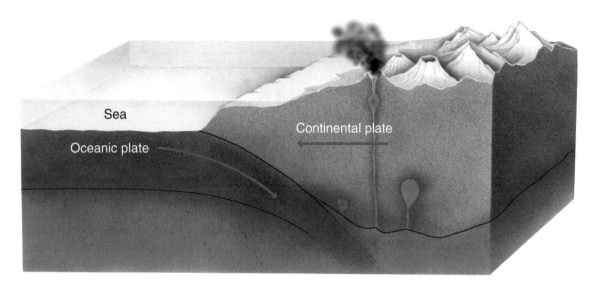

Sea

Oceanic plate

Continental plate

(a) Why is the oceanic plate forced beneath the continental plate?

.... (1 mark)

(b) What type of rock is formed when the continental crust is stressed at a plate boundary?

.... (1 mark)

(c) When oceanic and continental plates collide, as shown in the diagram, mountain ranges can be formed. Where, in the world, is this process forming mountain ranges today.

Circle one answer.

Iceland   West coast of South America   California   West coast of Africa   (1 mark)

(d) Give an example of a natural disaster which is associated with a convergent plate boundary.

....

.... (1 mark)

(e) Why can we not predict when an earthquake will next occur?

....

.... (1 mark)

Score   /5

How well did you do?
1–5   Try again
6–12   Getting there
13–16   Good work
17–22   Excellent!

TOTAL SCORE   /22

For more on this topic
see page 26 of your Success Guide

METALS

A

Choose just one answer, a, b, c or d.

1 Which of these metals is a liquid at room temperature?
(a) uranium   (c) mercury
(b) iron   (d) nickel   (1 mark)

2 What is the name given to Group I metals?
(a) alkali metals
(b) transition metals
(c) metalloids
(d) alkaline earth metals   (1 mark)

3 What colour are Group I compounds?
(a) white
(b) black
(c) green
(d) yellow   (1 mark)

4 Name the odd one out.
(a) iron
(b) sodium
(c) nickel
(d) gold   (1 mark)

5 Which of these statements is not true?
(a) Metals are strong.
(b) Metals are good conductors of heat.
(c) Metals have low melting points.
(d) Metals are ductile.   (1 mark)

Score /5

B

Answer all parts of the questions.

1 True or false?   True   False

(a) The element platinum is a liquid at room temperature.

(b) Group I metal compounds dissolve in water to form colourless solutions.

(c) Transition metal compounds are usually white.

(d) Transition metals and their compounds are often good catalysts.

(e) Transition metals are generally crumbly and soft.   (5 marks)

2 Metallic elements are found on the left of the periodic table.
Use the labels in the box to label sections a, b, and c of the periodic table below.   (3 marks)

Transition Metals
Group I
Group II

Section a
Section b
Section c
Section d
Section e

Score /8

30

C **These are GCSE-style questions. Answer all parts of the questions.**

1 Elements with similar properties are placed in the same group of the periodic table. Use the names given below to complete the table by placing each element in its correct group.

| iodine | | sodium | | copper |

Group I alkali metals	Transition metals	Group VII halogens
lithium	iron	chlorine
	nickel	bromine
potassium		

(3 marks)

2 These statements are all true of metals.

> • Metals are good conductors of heat.
>
> • Metals are good conductors of electricity.
>
> • Metals are shiny.
>
> • Metals are strong.

Using only the statements listed above, explain why metals are chosen for the following uses.

(a) Gold is used to make earrings.

....

(b) Copper is used to make saucepans.

....

(c) Steel is used to make bridges.

.... (3 marks)

3 This shows the periodic table split into five labelled sections.

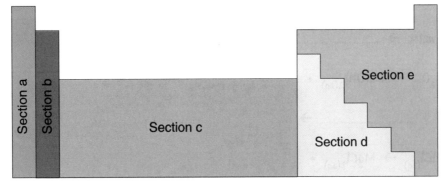

Section a
Section b
Section c
Section d
Section e

In which area of the periodic table are the non-metal elements found?

.... (1 mark)

Score   /7

How well did you do?

1–5	Try again
6–11	Getting there
12–15	Good work
16–20	Excellent!

TOTAL SCORE   /20

For more on this topic
see page 30 of your Success Guide

REACTIVITY SERIES

A

Choose just one answer, a, b, c or d.

1 How should lead be extracted from its ore?
(a) heating with carbon
(b) electrolysis
(c) react with water
(d) It is found as the pure metal in nature.
(1 mark)

2 How can sodium be extracted from its ore?
(a) heating with carbon
(b) electrolysis
(c) react with water
(d) It is found as the pure metal in nature.
(1 mark)

3 Name the gas found in air, which metals react with when they are burnt.
(a) oxygen   (c) carbon dioxide
(b) nitrogen   (d) argon   (1 mark)

4 What are the products formed when magnesium reacts with hydrochloric acid?
(a) magnesium oxide
(b) magnesium chloride + hydrogen
(c) magnesium chloride + water
(d) magnesium chloride   (1 mark)

5 Which of these metals would react most vigorously with dilute acid?
(a) zinc
(b) copper
(c) iron
(d) magnesium   (1 mark)

Score   /5

B

Answer all parts of the questions.

1 Complete the following word and symbol equations

(a) copper + oxygen → ....

(b) $2Cu_{(s)}$ + ...$_{(g)}$ → $2CuO_{(s)}$

(c) calcium + water → .... + hydrogen

(d) $Ca_{(s)}$ + $2H_2O_{(l)}$ → $Ca(OH)_{2(aq)}$ + ...$_{(g)}$

(e) Magnesium + ... → magnesium chloride + hydrogen

(f) $Mg_{(s)}$ + $2HCl_{(aq)}$ → $MgCl_{2(aq)}$ + ...$_{(g)}$ (6 marks)

2 (a) Which of these metals cannot be extracted by heating its ore with charcoal?   (1 mark)

zinc   iron   copper   sodium

(b) Which of these metals will react most slowly with air?   (1 mark)

zinc   iron   copper   sodium

(c) Which of these metals will not react with cold water?   (1 mark)

potassium   calcium   copper   sodium

Score   /9

C **These are GCSE-style questions. Answer all parts of the questions.**

1 Read the following passage carefully, then place the metals A, B, C and D in order of reactivity. Place the most reactive metal first.

Metal A displaced metal C from a solution of its sulphate.

Metal B reacts faster with hydrochloric acid than metal A.

Metal D does not react when it is heated with the oxide of metal C.

Most reactive   _____

_____

_____

Least reactive   _____

2 The diagram below shows the reactivity of four elements.   (1 mark)

Most reactive   Potassium

Carbon

Iron

Least reactive   Gold

Read each of the statements below. Then match each statement to the correct element.   (4 marks)

(a) This metal can be found in rivers and on the ground by itself. _____

(b) This is the only non metal element which conducts electricity. _____

(c) This metal must be extracted by electrolysis. _____

(d) This metal can be extracted from its ore by heating with charcoal. _____

Score   /5

How well did you do?

1–5   Try again
6–11   Getting there
12–15   Good work
16–19   Excellent!

TOTAL SCORE   /19

For more on this topic
see page 32 of your Success Guide

35

METAL DISPLACEMENT REACTIONS

A Choose just one answer, a, b, c or d.

1 Complete this equation.
iron + copper sulphate ➔
(a) iron, copper and sulphur
(b) iron sulphate
(c) iron sulphate + copper
(d) no reaction   (1 mark)

2 Which of these substances is required for steel to rust?
(a) water and iron
(b) zinc and magnesium
(c) water and oxygen
(d) iron and oxygen   (1 mark)

3 Which of these metals rust?
(a) copper   (c) All metals will rust eventually.
(b) magnesium (d) iron   (1 mark)

4 Aluminium is a fairly reactive metal. However, it does not react as quickly as might be suggested by the reactivity series. Why is this?
(a) Aluminium only reacts when oxygen is present.
(b) Aluminium is stored under oil.
(c) Aluminium reacts with oxygen to form a layer of aluminium oxide.
(d) Aluminium was only discovered relatively recently.   (1 mark)

5 Iron objects can be protected from rusting by sacrificial protection. Which of these metals could be attached to an iron object to prevent it from corroding?
(a) lead (b) gold (c) copper (d) zinc   (1 mark)

Score   /5

B Answer all parts of the questions.

1 Complete these word equations

(a) magnesium + copper sulphate ➔ .... + ...

(b) aluminium + iron oxide   ➔ .... + ...

(c) zinc + copper sulphate   ➔ .... + ...

(d) magnesium + zinc sulphate   ➔ .... + ...

(e) zinc + iron sulphate   ➔ .... + ...

2 Complete these formula equations.

(a) $Mg_{(s)}$ + $CuSO_{4(aq)}$ ➔ .... + ...

(b) $Zn_{(s)}$ + $FeSO_{4(aq)}$ ➔ .... + ...

(c) $Mg_{(s)}$ + $FeSO_{4(aq)}$ ➔ .... + ...

(d) $Zn_{(s)}$ + $CuSO_{4(aq)}$ ➔ .... + ...

(e) $Mg_{(s)}$ + $ZnSO_{4(aq)}$ ➔ .... + ...

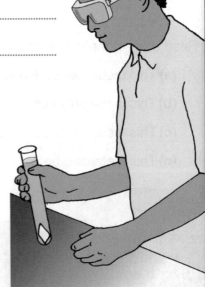

Score   /10

GCSE-style questions. Answer all parts of the questions.

1 A student had four different metals and four different metal sulphate solutions. She placed a couple of drops of each solution onto a spotting tile and then added a small piece of each metal. She recorded her results in the table below. A tick shows that a reaction has taken place, a cross shows that no reaction has taken place.

Metal/metal sulphate solution	Copper sulphate	Magnesium sulphate	Iron sulphate	Zinc sulphate
copper	—		✗	
magnesium	✔	—		✔
iron		✗	—	✗
zinc	✔	✗	✔	—

(a) Complete the table to show which reactions take place. (4 marks)

(b) Place the four metals in order of reactivity. (1 mark)

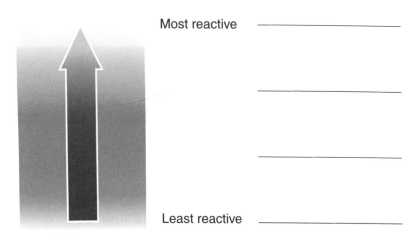

Most reactive _____

_____

_____

Least reactive _____

2 Choose two of the words below to complete the flow diagram.

carbon   copper

carbon dioxide   carbon monoxide   (2 marks)

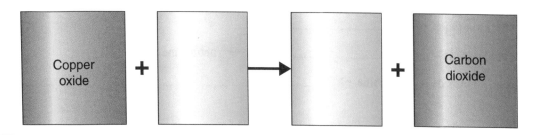

Copper oxide **+** [ ] → [ ] **+** Carbon dioxide

Score /7

How well did you do?
1–7 Try again
8–14 Getting there
15–18 Good work
19–22 Excellent!

TOTAL SCORE   /22

For more on this topic
see page 34 of your Success Guide

EXTRACTION OF IRON

METALS

A Choose just one answer, a, b, c or d.

1 Which of these metals can be found on its own (not in a compound)?
(a) potassium   (c) gold
(b) iron   (d) carbon   (1 mark)

2 Which of these substances is not a solid added to the blast furnace?
(a) iron ore   (c) coke
(b) carbon dioxide (d) limestone   (1 mark)

3 What is the name given to a reaction in which oxygen is removed?
(a) neutralisation
(b) reduction
(c) oxidation
(d) endothermic   (1 mark)

4 What is the name of the main ore of iron?
(a) iron
(b) magnetite
(c) galena
(d) haematite   (1 mark)

5 What is the name of the substance which actually reduces iron oxide to iron?
(a) carbon
(b) carbon dioxide
(c) coke
(d) carbon monoxide   (1 mark)

Score   /5

B Answer all parts of the questions.

1 Complete the following passage.

The main ore of iron is called .... It is a form of iron oxide with the formula .... Haematite often contains some impurities. The main impurity in haematite is normally.........................., which is often known as silica. When......................... is added to the blast .... it reacts with the silica to form a molten substance called......................... The .... has a .... density and floats on top of the molten iron. The slag can be collected and then used in.........................building or to make ....

(10 marks)

2 Complete the following word equations to show what happens in a Blast Furnace.

(a) Carbon + oxygen → ....

(b) Carbon dioxide + ... → carbon monoxide

(c) Carbon monoxide + iron oxide → .... + ...

(4 marks)

(d) Name two substances that are oxidised in the blast furnace.   (2 marks)

(e) Name two substances that are reduced in the blast furnace.   (2 marks)

Score   /18

C **This is a GCSE-style question. Answer all parts of the question.**

1 The diagram below shows a blast furnace which is used to extract iron from iron ore.

(a) Three solid raw materials are added to the blast furnace. One of the solid raw materials is iron ore. Name the other two.

....

....

(2 marks)

(b) The main chemical compound in iron ore is iron oxide. What is the name of the main ore of iron?

....

(1 mark)

Molton iron

(c) What is the other raw material added to the blast furnace?

.... (1 mark)

(d) What actually reduces the iron oxide to iron?

.... (1 mark)

(e) In the blast furnace iron is extracted from iron ore. Which of these options best describes this reaction? Tick one box.

Electrolysis ☐

Reduction ☐

Oxidation ☐

Neutralisation ☐

(f) In the blast furnace, what does the limestone do?

....

....

....

.... (2 marks)

Score /7

How well did you do?

1–11   Try again
12–17 Getting there
18–25 Good work
26–30 Excellent!

TOTAL SCORE   /30

For more on this topic see page 36 of your Success Guide

37

PURIFICATION OF COPPER AND EXTRACTION OF ALUMINIUM

Choose just one answer, a, b, c or d.

1 **Which of these metals is the most reactive?**
(a) zinc (c) copper
(b) iron (d) aluminium (1 mark)

2 **Which of these metals is the least reactive?**
(a) zinc
(b) iron
(c) copper
(d) aluminium (1 mark)

3 **During electrolysis, what is the name given to the negative electrode?**
(a) metal
(b) negatode
(c) anode
(d) cathode (1 mark)

4 **What is the main ore of aluminium?**
(a) cryolite
(b) magnetite
(c) dolomite
(d) bauxite (1 mark)

5 **Why is aluminium extracted from its ore by electrolysis?**
(a) Aluminium is less reactive than carbon.
(b) Aluminium is more reactive than carbon.
(c) Electrolysis is cheap.
(d) Electrolysis is hard to spell. (1 mark)

Score /5

B

Answer all parts of the questions.

1 The diagram below shows how aluminium can be extracted from its ore by electrolysis. Label the diagram using the labels shown in the box.

positive ion

negative ion

positive electrode

negative electrode

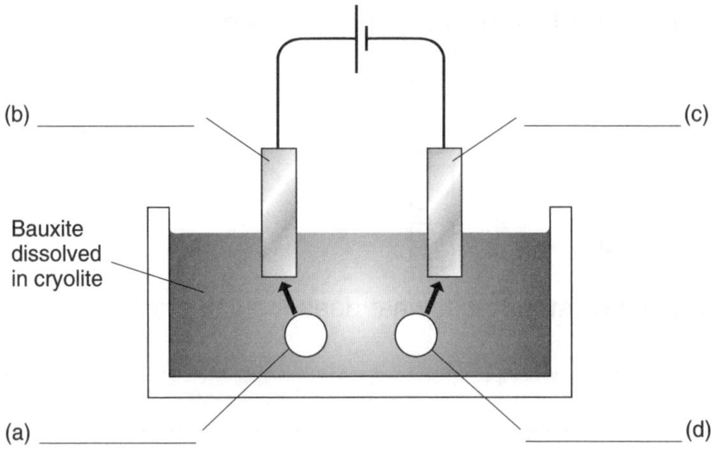

(b) _____

(c) _____

Bauxite dissolved in cryolite

(a) _____

(d) _____

(4 marks)

2 True or false?

	True	False
(a) The main ore of aluminium is haematite.	☐	☐
(b) During electrolysis metal ions go to the negative electrode.	☐	☐
(c) During the electrolysis of copper sulphate, copper is deposited at the positive electrode.	☐	☐
(d) Cryolite is an ore of copper.	☐	☐
(e) Electrolysis is cheaper than heating with carbon.	☐	☐

(5 marks)

Score /9

C **This is a GCSE-style question. Answer all parts of the question.**

1 The diagram below shows how the metal aluminium can be extracted from aluminium oxide.

(a) What name is given to this process?

.... (1 mark)

(b) Name the main ore of aluminium.

.... (1 mark)

(c) Name the other ore of aluminium that is also used in the extraction of aluminium.

.... (1 mark)

(d) Why is the other ore of aluminium used?

.... (1 mark)

(e) During the electrolysis of aluminium oxide, the aluminium ions move. Which electrode do these ions move towards?

.... (1 mark)

(f) Which of these words best describes what happens to aluminium ions during electrolysis?

Tick one box.

displacement ☐

reduction ☐

oxidation ☐

neutralisation ☐   (1 mark)

(g) During the electrolysis of aluminium oxide the oxide ions also move. Which electrode do these ions move towards?

.... (1 mark)

(h) On the diagram above, label the positive electrode.

.... (1 mark)

(i) What material is the positive electrode made from?

.... (1 mark)

(j) Why must the positive electrodes be periodically replaced?

....

.... (2 marks)

Score   /11

How well did you do?

1–7   Try again
8–14   Getting there
15–20 Good work
21–25 Excellent!

TOTAL SCORE   /25

For more on this topic
see page 38 of your Success Guide

PURIFICATION OF COPPER AND EXTRACTION OF ALUMINIUM

39

ACIDS AND ALKALIS

A

Choose just one answer, a, b, c or d.

1 What does the pH of a solution show?
(a) its colour
(b) its density
(c) its smell
(d) the concentration of hydrogen ions

1 mark)

2 What is the pH of a strong acid?
(a) 1
(b) 7
(c) 6
(d) 14

(1 mark)

3 What is the pH of a neutral solution?
(a) 1
(b) 7
(c) 6
(d) 14

(1 mark)

4 What is the pH of a weak acid?
(a) 1   (c) 6
(b) 7   (d) 14

(1 mark)

5 What is formed when sulphuric acid reacts with sodium hydroxide?
(a) sodium sulphate and hydrogen
(b) sodium sulphate and water
(c) sodium chloride and water
(d) sodium chloride and hydrogen

(1 mark)

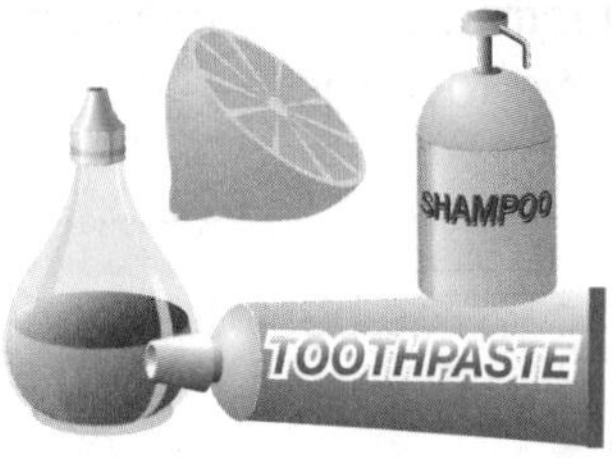

Score   /5

B

Answer all parts of the questions.

1 Complete these word equations.

(a) nitric acid + sodium hydroxide → .... + ...

(b) sulphuric acid + potassium hydroxide → ....+ ....

(c) hydrochloric acid + ... → sodium chloride + ...   (6 marks)

2 Name the odd one out.

(a) | potassium hydroxide | sulphuric acid | ammonia solution | sodium hydroxide |

(b) | lemon juice | hydrochloric acid | calcium hydroxide | nitric acid |

(c) | methyl orange | ammonia solution | Universal indicator | blue litmus | (3 marks)

Nitric Acid   Sodium Hydroxide   Hydrochloric Acid   Ammonia Solution

Score   /9

C

This is a GCSE-style question. Answer all parts of the question.

1 Indicators are chemicals that can be used to tell whether a solution is acidic, alkaline or neutral by the way they change colour. Universal Indicator, methyl orange and phenolphthalein are three widely used and useful indicators. The three tables below show the colours of these three indicators in different pH solutions.

Universal Indicator

pH	Colour
1 – 2	red
3 – 5	orange
6	yellow
7	green
8 – 9	blue
10 – 14	purple

Methyl orange

pH	Colour
1 – 3	red
4 – 14	yellow

Phenolphthalein

pH	Colour
1 – 9	colourless
10 – 14	violet

(a) What colour is the indicator phenolphthalein in a solution of pH 6?

.... (1 mark)

(b) What colour is the indicator Universal Indicator in a solution of pH 8?

.... (1 mark)

(c) What colour is the indicator methyl orange in a solution of pH 10?

.... (1 mark)

(d) Which of these indicators could be used to identify a neutral solution?

.... (1 mark)

(e) What colour would the indicator you have named be in a neutral solution?

.... (1 mark)

(f) Which two indicators could be used to differentiate between a strong acid and a weak acid?

.... (1 mark)

(g) Which two indicators could be used to differentiate between a strong alkali and a weak alkali?

.... (1 mark)

Score   /7

How well did you do?

1–5   Try again
6–11 Getting there
12–15 Good work
16–21 Excellent!

TOTAL SCORE   /21

**For more on this topic
see page 40 of your Success Guide**

MAKING SALTS

A Choose just one answer, a, b, c or d.

1 Which of these chemicals is a base?
(a) lemon juice   (c) sulphuric acid
(b) hydrochloric acid (d) calcium carbonate
(1 mark)

2 Name the products formed when zinc reacts with hydrochloric acid.
(a) zinc sulphate + water
(b) zinc chloride + water
(c) zinc sulphate + hydrogen
(d) zinc chloride + hydrogen   (1 mark)

3 Name the products formed when zinc oxide reacts with hydrochloric acid.
(a) zinc sulphate + water
(b) zinc chloride + water
(c) zinc sulphate + hydrogen
(d) zinc chloride + hydrogen   (1 mark)

4 Name the products formed when zinc carbonate reacts with sulphuric acid.
(a) zinc sulphate + water + carbon dioxide
(b) copper nitrate + water + carbon dioxide
(c) zinc sulphate + hydrogen
(d) zinc sulphate + water   (1 mark)

5 Name the products formed when copper oxide reacts with hydrochloric acid.
(a) copper sulphate
(b) copper chloride + hydrogen
(c) copper chloride + water
(d) copper sulphate + water   (1 mark)

Score   /5

B Answer all parts of the questions.

1 Complete the following word equations.

(a) zinc + sulphuric acid → zinc sulphate + ...

(b) .... + hydrochloric acid → magnesium chloride + hydrogen

(c) copper carbonate + sulphuric acid → .... + water + carbon dioxide

(d) zinc carbonate + nitric acid → zinc nitrate + ... + ...

(e) zinc oxide + nitric acid → zinc nitrate + ...

(f) copper oxide + ... → copper sulphate + water   (7 marks)

2 The instructions below show the steps needed to make the salt copper chloride from copper carbonate and hydrochloric acid, but the order of the steps has been jumbled up!

Put the sentences in the correct order to explain how the salt can be made.

(a) It is heated until the first crystals appear.

(b) Copper carbonate is added to the acid until it stops fizzing.

(c) The solution is poured into an evaporating dish.

(d) The solution is left for a few days for the copper chloride to crystallise.

(e) The unreacted copper carbonate is removed by filtering.   (5 marks)

Score   /12

C These are GCSE-style questions. Answer all parts of the questions.

1 Which two of the following are produced when calcium reacts with water?

| more water | calcium oxide | oxygen | calcium hydroxide | hydrogen |

(2 marks)

2 Which two of the following are produced when zinc oxide reacts with hydrochloric acid?

| hydrogen | oxygen | water | zinc chloride | carbon dioxide |

(2 marks)

3 The table below shows the names and formulae of six compounds.

Name of compound	Formula of compound
hydrochloric acid	HCl
sulphuric acid	H_2SO_4
copper oxide	CuO
copper carbonate	$CuCO_3$
copper sulphate	$CuSO_4$
copper chloride	$CuCl_2$

(a) Complete the word equation below to show the reaction between copper carbonate and sulphuric acid.

Copper carbonate + sulphuric acid → .... + ... + ... (3 marks)

(b) Complete and balance the equations below to show the reactions between

(i) copper oxide and sulphuric acid.

$CuO + H_2SO_4$ → .... + ... (2 marks)

(ii) calcium carbonate and sulphuric acid

$CaCO_3 + H_2SO_4$ → .... + ... + ... (3 marks)

(iii) zinc oxide and hydrochloric acid

$ZnO + 2HCl$ → .... + ... (2 marks)

Score   /14

How well did you do?

1–9   Try again
10–15 Getting there
16–23 Good work
24–31 Excellent!

TOTAL SCORE   /31

For more on this topic
see page 42 of your Success Guide

STATES OF MATTER

A
Choose just one answer, a, b, c or d.

1 Which of these statements best describes a solid?
- **(a)** Solids have a fixed volume but do not have a fixed shape.
- **(b)** Solids have a fixed volume and a fixed shape.
- **(c)** Solids have a fixed shape but do not have a fixed volume.
- **(d)** Solids will fill any container they are placed in. (1 mark)

2 Which of these statements best describes a liquid?
- **(a)** Liquids have a fixed volume but do not have a fixed shape.
- **(b)** Liquids have a fixed volume and a fixed shape.
- **(c)** Liquids have a fixed shape but do not have a fixed volume.
- **(d)** Liquids will fill any container they are placed in. (1 mark)

3 Which of these statements best describes a gas?
- **(a)** Gases have a fixed volume but do not have a fixed shape.
- **(b)** Gases have a fixed volume and a fixed shape.
- **(c)** Gases have a fixed shape but do not have a fixed volume.
- **(d)** Gases will fill any container into which they are placed. (1 mark)

4 The forces of attraction between particles are strongest in:
- **(a)** Solids
- **(b)** Liquids
- **(c)** Gases
- **(d)** Plasmas (1 mark)

5 The change of state between gas and liquid is called:
- **(a)** Freezing
- **(b)** Melting
- **(c)** Condensing
- **(d)** Evaporating (1 mark)

Score /5

B
Answer all parts of the question.

1 Abi measures the temperature of some ice every minute as it is heated. Her results are shown in the table.

Time (minutes)	0	1	2	3	4	5	6	7	8	9	10
Temperature (°C)	−5	−3	−1	0	0	0	0	2	4	7	9

(a) Plot these results on the axes opposite. (1 mark)

(b) What is happening during the first three minutes of Abi's experiment?
.... (1 mark)

(c) What is happening between the minutes three and six?
.... (1 mark)

(d) What happens after the seventh minute?
.... (1 mark)

(e) What is the melting point of ice?
.... (1 marks)

(f) What is the freezing point of water?
.... (1 marks)

Score /6

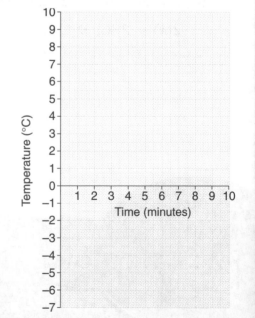

44

C This is a GCSE-style question. Answer all parts of the question.

1 A scientist has discovered a new compound, 'X'.

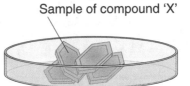
Sample of compound 'X'

X is a solid at room temperature. The scientist heated a sample of X for 20 minutes and recorded her results below.

Time (mins)	0	2	4	6	8	10	12	14	16	18	20
Temperature (°C)	25	32	40	40	40	40	42	45	48	51	53

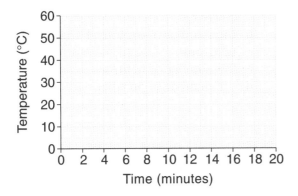

(a) Plot the scientist's results on the axes above. (2 marks)

(b) What is the melting point of the new compound?

.... (1 mark)

(c) What is the change of state which occurs when compound 'X' melts?

.... to .... (1 mark)

(d) If the compound is heated further it eventually boils. What is the change of state that occurs when compound 'X' boils?

.... to .... (1 mark)

Score /5

How well did you do?
1–5 Try again
6–10 Getting there
11–14 Good work
15–16 Excellent!

TOTAL SCORE /16

For more on this topic
see page 46 of your Success Guide

ATOMIC STRUCTURE

A

Choose just one answer, a, b, c or d.

1 Protons are small particles which have:
(a) a mass of 1 and a charge of −1
(b) a mass of 1 and a charge of +1
(c) a negligible mass and a charge of −1
(d) a mass of 1 but no charge   (1 mark)

2 Neutrons are small particles which have:
(a) a mass of 1 and a charge of −1
(b) a mass of 1 and a charge of +1
(c) a negligible mass and a charge of −1
(d) a mass of 1 but no charge   (1 mark)

3 Electrons are very small particles which have:
(a) a mass of 1 and a charge of −1
(b) a mass of 1 and a charge of +1
(c) a negligible mass and a charge of −1
(d) a mass of 1 but no charge   (1 mark)

4 The mass number of an atom is:
(a) the number of protons – the number of electrons
(b) the number of protons + the number of neutrons
(c) the number of neutrons
(d) the number of protons   (1 mark)

5 The atomic number of an atom is:
(a) the number of protons – the number of electrons
(b) the number of protons + the number of neutrons
(c) the number of neutrons
(d) the number of protons   (1 mark)

Score   /5

B

Answer all parts of the questions.

1 Complete the following passage.

Protons and neutrons are found in the .... of an atom. Protons have a mass of

.... and a charge of .... Neutrons are also found in the nucleus of atoms.

These particles have a mass of .... and no charge. Electrons are found in ....

around the nucleus. Electrons have a .... mass and a charge of .... (7 marks)

2 (a) Complete the following table to show the number of protons, neutrons and electrons present

	Protons	Neutrons	Electrons
$^{35}_{17}Cl$			
$^{37}_{17}Cl$			

(6 marks)

(b) What is the name given to atoms of the same element that have different numbers of neutrons?

.... (1 mark)

3 An atom of an element has 11 electrons.

(a) What is the name of the element? ....

(b) What is the electron structure of an atom of this element? ....

(c) To which group of the periodic table does it belong? .... (3 marks)

Score   /17

46

C

These are GCSE-style questions. Answer all parts of the questions.

1 The diagrams below show two atoms of the element oxygen. Atoms of oxygen contain three types of particle. The particles in the atoms have been represented by the symbols ✖ , ○ and ◉ .

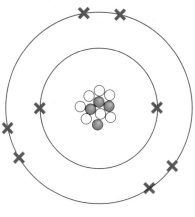

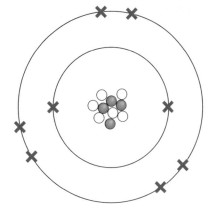

Oxygen – 18   Oxygen – 16

(a) What type of particles do the symbols 'X' on the diagrams represent?

.... (1 mark)

(b) The symbols ○ and ◉ are found in the centre of the two oxygen atoms.

(i) What is the centre of an atom called?

.... (1 mark)

(ii) What type of particles do the symbols ○ and ◉ on the diagrams represent?

.... (1 mark)

2 The table shows some information about the two oxygen atoms shown in the diagrams above.

Complete the table to show the number of protons, neutrons, electrons, and the electron structure of each of the oxygen atoms.

	Number of protons	Number of neutrons	Number of electrons	Electron structure
$^{16}_{8}O$		8		2,6
$^{18}_{8}O$		10		

(5 marks)

Score   /8

How well did you do?

1–11   Try again
12–17   Getting there
18–25   Good work
26–30   Excellent!

TOTAL SCORE   /30

For more on this topic
see page 48 of your Success Guide

IONIC AND COVALENT BONDING

A

Choose just one answer, a, b, c or d.

1 Which group of the periodic table has atoms that have a full outer shell of electrons?
(a) Group I   (c) Group VII
(b) Group II   (d) Group 0   (1 mark)

2 If a sodium atom loses an electron to form an ion, what is its charge?
(a) 1+
(b) 2+
(c) 0
(d) 1–   (1 mark)

3 If a chlorine atom gains an electron to form an ion, what is its charge?
(a) 1+
(b) 2+
(c) 0
(d) 1–   (1 mark)

4 What type of bonding occurs between sodium and chlorine?
(a) covalent
(b) metallic
(c) molecular
(d) ionic   (1 mark)

5 A metal forms a compound in which the metal is an ion with a 1+ charge. To which group does this element belong?
(a) Group I
(b) Group II
(c) Group VII
(d) Group 0   (1 mark)

Score   /5

B

Answer all parts of the question.

1 Sodium reacts with chlorine to form the ionic compound sodium chloride. The dot and cross diagrams of sodium and chlorine are shown below.

(a) Draw a dot and cross diagram to show the electron arrangement in a sodium ion and a chloride ion.

(2 marks)

(b) What is an ion? .... (1 mark)

(c) What is the charge on a chloride ion?.. (1 mark)

(d) Is there any difference between the electrons drawn as dots and the electrons drawn as crosses?

....

(1 mark)

(e) What is an ionic bond?

....

(1 mark)

Score   /6

48

GCSE SUCCESS

VISUAL REVISION GUIDE

QUESTIONS & ANSWERS

BRAND NEW

CHEMISTRY

Emma Poole

ANSWER BOOK

LIMESTONE

Section A
1 (a)
2 (a)
3 (d)
4 (c)
5 (b)

Section B
1 (a) carbon dioxide
  (b) calcium hydroxide
  (c) CaO
  (d) $Ca(OH)_2$
2 (a) t
  (b) f
  (c) f
  (d) t
  (e) f

Section C
1 (a) limestone
  (b) glass
  (c) quicklime
  (d) limewater
2 (a) thermal
    decomposition
  (b) CaO, CO_2
3 Heating a mixture of
  limestone, sand and
  soda until it melts

ROCKS

Section A
1 (d)
2 (c)
3 (d)
4 (a)
5 (b)

Section B
1 biotite schist – folded
  bands of black and
  brown crystals –
  metamorphic
  syenite – coarse grained
  interlocking pink, grey
  and white crystals –
  igneous
  conglomerate –
  rounded pebbles of
  quartz and flint in a
  matrix of much finer
  grains of silt and sand –
  sedimentary
2 The remains/imprint/
  impressions of a living
  thing.

Section C
1 (a) X
  (b) formed more slowly

(c) sedimentary
(d) metamorphic
(e) They were made
    from different
    rocks.
(f) marble
2 (d) (e)
  (c) (b)
  (a)

CLUES IN ROCKS

Section A
1 (b)
2 (c)
3 (a)
4 (a)
5 (d)

Section B
1 Basalt, sandstone,
  ironstone, limestone,
  dolomite
2 Forces, fold, fault

Section C
1 (newest)
  Limestone is deposited
  Sandstone is deposited.
  Mudstone is deposited.
  Rocks are folded.
  Rocks are weathered.
  Dolomite is deposited .
  (oldest).
2 (a) faulted
  (b) tilted
  (c) folded, weathered

FOSSIL FUELS

Section A
1 (d)
2 (c)
3 (d)
4 (b)
5 (c)

Section B
1 (c)
  (a)
  (d)
  (e)
  (b)
2 (a) t
  (b) f
  (c) f
  (d) t
  (e) f

Section C
1 (a) hydrogen and
    carbon
  (b) fractional
    distillation

(c) refinery gas
(d) refinery gas
(e) bitumen
2 molecule c

CRACKING

Section A
1 (d)   2 (a)   3 (d)
4 (b)   5 (d)

Section B
1 (a) i = ethene
    ii = propene
    iii = propane
    iv = ethane
  (b) (iii) and (iv)
  (c) (i) and (ii)
  (d) (i) and (ii)
  (e) orange/brown to
    colourless

Section C
1 (a) fractional
    distillation
  (b) cracking
2 (a) c
  (b) ethane
  (c) a
  (d) c

PLASTICS

Section A
1 (d)
2 (b)
3 (a)
4 (a)
5 (a)

Section B
1 (a) f
  (b) f
  (c) f
  (d) t
  (e) t
2

(a)

(b)

Section C
1 (a) compound c
  (b) bags/bottles
2 (a) molecule c
  (b) methane
  (c) polypropene

EVOLUTION OF THE ATMOSPHERE

Section A
1 (a)
2 (b)
3 (b)
4 (b)
5 (c)

Section B
1 (a) 3
  (b) 5
  (c) 1
  (d) 4
  (e) 2
2 The carbon dioxide
  reacts with seawater to
  form carbonate
  /hydrogen carbonate
  salts.

Section C
1 (a) (i) Oxygen
    (ii) Nitrogen
    (iii) Other gases
  (b) steam/ammonia
    /methane
  (c) volcanic activity
  (d) plants evolved
  (e) ozone layer
  (f) carbonate

POLLUTION OF THE ATMOSPHERE

Section A
1 (b)
2 (c)
3 (d)

4 (d)
5 (b)

Section B

1 Greenhouse effect – carbon dioxide – ice caps melt, causing massive flooding
The hole in the ozone layer – CFCs – skin cancers in animals and damage to crops
Acid rain – sulphur dioxide – damage to lakes, trees and buildings

2 It forms a layer around the Earth, which traps heat energy from the Sun.

3 Many fossil fuels contain sulphur. When sulphur is burnt, sulphur dioxide is made

Section C

1 (a) It's increasing as we burn more fossil fuels.
 (b) Many fossil fuels contain a little sulphur. When they are burnt, sulphur dioxide is produced. This dissolves in rain water to form acid rain.
 (c) damage to statues and damage to trees.
 (d) holes in the ozone layer

2 (a) Greenhouse effect
 (b) disruption to weather patterns /farming/droughts/ ice caps melting/floods

POLLUTION OF THE ENVIRONMENT

Section A

1 (a)
2 (c)
3 (b)
4 (b)
5 (c)

Section B

1 (a) (iii), (i), (v), (ii), (iv)

 (b) eutrophication
 (c) blue baby disease/stomach cancer

Section C

1 (a) sedimentary
 (b) building material/neutralise acidic soils or lakes/glass/cement/c oncrete
 (c) advantages: new jobs/brings money in to an area disadvantages: new roads/increased traffic/dust/damage to wildlife or landscape

STRUCTURE OF THE EARTH AND PLATE TECTONICS

Section A

1 (b)
2 (d)
3 (c)
4 (c)
5 (b)

Section B

1 (a) crust
 (b) mantle
 (c) lithosphere
 (d) outer core
 (e) inner core
2 (a) t
 (b) f
 (c) f
 (d) t
 (e) t

Section C

1 (a) Inner core – a
 Outer core – d
 Crust – b
 Mantle – c
 (b) lithosphere
 (c) (i) iron and nickel
 (ii) liquid
 (iii) solid

MOVING PLATES

Section A

1 (d)
2 (a)
3 (c)
4 (c)
5 (a)

Section B

1 (c)
 (e)
 (d)
 (b)
 (d)
2 Jigsaw fit of South America and Africa, similar fossil remains in South America and Africa, similar rock strata in South America and Africa, rock record shows Britain has moved through different climatic zones.

Section C

1 (a) crust and upper mantle
 (b) Jigsaw fit of South America and Africa, similar fossil remains in South America and Africa, similar rock strata in South America and Africa.
2 As the plates move apart, magma comes to the surface. When the magma cools, it forms the rock basalt. Roughly every half a million years the magnetic pole reverses and the iron in the basalt lines up in the opposite direction. The rock record shows that the Earth's plates have been moving relatively to each other for a very long time.

PLATE BOUNDARIES

Section A

1 (b)
2 (c)
3 (a)
4 (d)
5 (b)

Section B

1 (a) oceanic plate
 (b) continental plate
 (c) volcano
 (d) fold mountain
 (e) melting
2 boundaries, slide, San Andreas, plates, stuck, forces, earthquake

Section C

1 (a) it is more dense
 (b) metamorphic
 (c) West coast of South America
 (d) Earthquake/volcano
 (e) Too many factors are involved.

METALS

Section A

1 (c) 2 (a) 3 (a)
4 (b) 5 (c)

Section B

1 (a) f
 (b) t
 (c) f
 (d) t
 (e) f
2 Transition metals = c
 Group I = a
 Group II = b

Section C

1 iodine = Group VII halogen
 sodium = Group I alkali metal
 copper = transition metal
2 (a) Metals are shiny.
 (b) Metals are good conductors of heat.
 (c) Metals are strong.
3 Section e

REACTIVITY SERIES

Section A

1 (a)   4 (b)
2 (b)   5 (d)
3 (a)

Section B

1 (a) copper oxide
 (b) O_2
 (c) calcium hydroxide
 (d) H_2
 (e) hydrochloric acid
 (f) H_2
2 (a) sodium
 (b) copper
 (c) copper

Section C

1 B, A, C, D
2 (a) gold
 (b) carbon
 (c) sodium
 (d) iron

METAL DISPLACEMENT REACTIONS

Section A
1 (c)
2 (c)
3 (d)
4 (c)
5 (d)

Section B
1 (a) magnesium sulphate + copper
  (b) aluminium oxide + iron
  (c) zinc sulphate + copper
  (d) magnesium sulphate + zinc
  (e) zinc sulphate + iron
2 (a) $Cu_{(s)} + MgSO_{4(aq)}$
  (b) $Fe_{(s)} + ZnSO_{4(aq)}$
  (c) $Fe_{(s)} + MgSO_{4(aq)}$
  (d) $Cu_{(s)} + ZnSO_{4(aq)}$
  (e) $Zn_{(s)} + MgSO_{4(aq)}$

Section C
1 (a) crosses for copper+ magnesium sulphate and copper + zinc sulphate
    ticks for magnesium+ iron sulphate and iron+copper sulphate
  (b) magnesium, zinc, iron, copper
2 carbon, copper

EXTRACTION OF IRON

Section A
1 (c)
2 (b)
3 (b)
4 (d)
5 (d)

Section B
1 haematite, Fe_2O_3, silicon dioxide, limestone, furnace, slag, slag, lower, road, fertilisers
2 (a) carbon dioxide
  (b) carbon
  (c) iron, carbon dioxide
  (d) carbon and carbon monoxide
  (e) iron oxide and carbon dioxide

Section C
1 (a) coke and limestone
  (b) haematite
  (c) hot air
  (d) carbon monoxide
  (e) reduction
  (f) reacts with impurities 'silica' to form slag.

PURIFICATION OF COPPER AND EXTRACTION OF ALUMINIUM

Section A
1 (d)
2 (c)
3 (d)
4 (d)
5 (b)

Section B
1 (a) positive ion – d
    negative ion – a
    positive electrode– b
    negative electrode– c
2 (a) f
  (b) t
  (c) f
  (d) f
  (e) f

Section C
1 (a) electrolysis
  (b) bauxite
  (c) cryolite
  (d) It has a lower melting point, and bauxite dissolves in molten cryolite.
  (e) negative
  (f) reduction
  (g) positive
  (h) blue section labelled
  (i) graphite
  (j) The oxygen that is formed there reacts with the carbon to form carbon dioxide. So the graphite electrode is eaten away.

ACIDS AND ALKALIS

Section A
1 (d)
2 (a)
3 (b)
4 (c)
5 (b)

Section B
1 (a) sodium nitrate + water
  (b) potassium sulphate + water
  (c) sodium hydroxide + water
2 (a) sulphuric acid
  (b) calcium hydroxide
  (c) ammonia solution

Section C
1 (a) colourless
  (b) blue
  (c) yellow
  (d) Universal Indicator
  (e) green
  (f) Universal Indicator and methyl orange
  (g) Universal Indicator and phenolpht halein

MAKING SALTS

Section A
1 (d)
2 (d)
3 (b)
4 (a)
5 (c)

Section B
1 (a) hydrogen
  (b) magnesium
  (c) copper sulphate
  (d) carbon dioxide + water
  (e) water
  (f) sulphuric acid
2 (a) 4
  (b) 1
  (c) 3
  (d) 5
  (e) 2

Section C
1 calcium hydroxide, hydrogen
2 zinc chloride, water
3 (a) copper sulphate + water + carbon dioxide
  (b) (i) $CuSO_4 + H_2O$
      (ii) $CaSO_4 + H_2O + CO_2$
      (iii) $ZnCl_2 + H_2O$

STATES OF MATTER

Section A
1 (b)
2 (a)
3 (d)
4 (a)
5 (c)

Section B
1 (a)
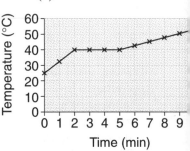
  (b) The ice is warming up.
  (c) The ice is melting to form liquid water.
  (d) The liquid water starts to warm up.
  (e) 0 °C
  (f) 0 °C

Section C
1 (a)

  (b) 40 °C
  (c) solid to liquid
  (d) liquid to gas

ATOMIC STRUCTURE

Section A
1 (b)
2 (d)
3 (c)
4 (b)
5 (d)

Section B
1 nucleus, one, 1^+, one, shells/levels, negligible, 1^-
2 (a) 17,18,17 17, 20,17
  (b) isotopes
3 (a) sodium
  (b) 2, 8, 1
  (c) Group I

Section C
1 (a) electrons
  (b) (i) nucleus
      (ii) protons and neutrons

3 8,8
  8,8 2,6

IONIC AND COVALENT BONDING

Section A
1 (d)   2 (a)   3 (d)   4 (d)
5 (a)

Section B
1 (a)

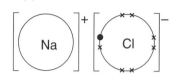

(b) a charged atom (atom which has gained or lost an electron or electrons)
(c) 1–
(d) They are all identical
(e) The attraction between oppositely-charged ions.

Section C
(a)

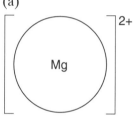

(b)

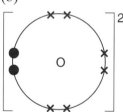

IONIC AND COVALENT COMPOUNDS

Section A
1 (c)
2 (b)
3 (d)
4 (a)
5 (a)

Section B
1 (a)

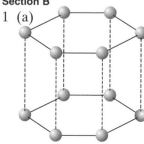

(b)(i) Each carbon atom is bonded to four other carbon atoms by strong covalent bonds.
(ii) Each carbon atom is bonded to three other carbon atoms in the same layer by strong covalent bonds, but the bonding between layers is weak.

Section C
1 (a) molecule, one, electrons
(b)

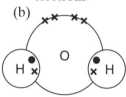

(c) There are strong covalent bonds within water molecules. But only weak forces of attraction between water molecules.

PERIODIC TABLE

Section A
1 (c)
2 (b)
3 (c)
4 (b)
5 (a)

SECTION B
1 (a) atomic
(b) groups
(c) number of electron shells
(d) III
(e) Group
2 He left gaps for elements that had not yet been discovered and made predictions about their properties. Occasionally he swapped the order of elements, so that elements with similar properties lined up in the same group.

3 It has not been discovered yet

Section C
1 (a) They had not been discovered.
(b) (i)   Tellurium – Group VII
    (ii) Iodine – Group VI
(c) Because of the properties, iodine was similar to the other elements in Group VII and tellurium was similar to the other elements in Group VI.
(d) increasing atomic number

TRANSITION METALS

Section A
1 (b)
2 (b)
3 (c)
4 (b)
5 (a)

Section B
1 (a)

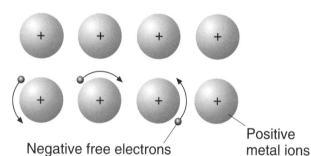

Negative free electrons   Positive metal ions

(b) A free electron is not bound to one atom but can move through the whole structure.
(c) Good conductor of heat/ electricity – free electrons can move through structure or malleable/ductile – free electrons allow atoms to slide over each other.

Section C
1 ionic, white, colourless, transition, pottery glazes, catalysts, iron

2 iron – strong – bridges
  nickel – hardwearing – coins
  copper – good conductor of heat – saucepans
3 strong – can support heavy loads
  high melting point – do not form liquids until they are very hot good conductor of electricity – an electric current can pass through them easily.

THE ALKALI METALS

Section A
1 (b)
2 (c)
3 (c)
4 (c)
5 (d)

Section B
1 (a) f
(b) t
(c) t
(d) t
(e) t
2 (a) lithium hydroxide
(b) H_2
(c) water
(d) $2Na$, H_2
(e) hydrogen
(f) $2K$

Section C
1 (a) sodium hydroxide, hydrogen
(b) (i)   purple
    (ii) an alkaline solution
(c) (i)   They are both in Group I which means they both have one outer electron.
    (ii) potassium

The outer electron is further from the nucleus in a potassium atom than in a sodium atom so can be lost more easily.

THE HALOGENS

Section A
1 (a)
2 (c)
3 (d)
4 (b)
5 (a)

Section B
1 (a) f (b) f (c) t (d) f
  (e) t
2 (a) potassium chloride + iodine
  (b) 2KCl
  (c) potassium chloride + bromine
  (d) $2KCl + Br_2$

Section C
1 (a) water purification /bleach
  (b) less reactive down the group, extra electron shells means it is harder to attract electrons down the group
  (c) (i) potassium iodide + chlorine → potassium chloride + iodine
    (ii) $2KI_{(aq)} + Cl_{2(g)} \rightarrow 2KCl_{(aq)} + I_{2(g)}$

NOBLE GASES

Section A
1 (d)
2 (a)
3 (d)
4 (d)
5 (a)

Section B
1

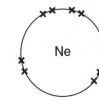

2 (a) electron
  (b) do not
  (c) increases
  (d) increase
  (e) monatomic
  (f) colourless

Section C
1 Xenon has a full outer shell of electrons. It does not react because it does it does not need to lose or gain electrons.
2 far right-hand column shaded
3 balloons/airships
4 Two chlorine atoms can be joined by a single covalent bond to make a chlorine molecule. Argon atoms already have a full outer shell of electrons so do not react.

ELECTROLYSIS OF BRINE

Section A
1 (c)
2 (d)
3 (b)
4 (c)
5 (b)

Section B
1 Sodium hydroxide solution = (e)
  Negative electrode = (d)
  Positive electrode = (a)
  Hydrogen gas = (c)
  Chlorine gas = (b)
2 (a) t
  (b) f
  (c) t
  (d) f
  (e) t

Section C
1 (a) chlorine
  (b) $2Cl^- \rightarrow Cl_2 + 2e^-$
  (c) sterilise water/bleach/

hydrochloric acid/PVC
  (d) hydrogen
  (e) $2H^+ + 2e^- \rightarrow H_2$
  (f) manufacture of margarine
  (g) sodium hydroxide
  (h) manufacture of soap/detergents/rayon/ acetate

COMMON TESTS AND SAFETY HAZARDS

Section A
1 (d) 2 (a) 3 (c)
4 (b) 5 (a)

Section B
Carbon dioxide, bubbled, milky/cloudy, lighted, 'squeaky pop', oxygen, air, glowing, relights

Section C
1 Corrosive – (b)
  Harmful – (d)
  Highly flammable – (a)
  Toxic – (c)
2 Damp litmus is bleached.

RATES OF REACTION

Section A
1 (a)
2 (d)
3 (b)
4 (a)
5 (a)

Section B
1 (a)

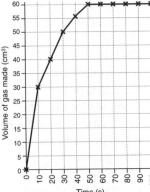

(b) start/0–10 seconds
(c) after 50 seconds

Section C
1 (a) mass balance /collect over water with a calibrated measuring cylinder, etc. / gas syringe with calibration
  (b) timer/stopwatch
  (c) volume/mass of gas produced every time period, e.g. 10 seconds
  (d) (i) 20 °C
    (ii) Particles have less energy/move more slowly, collide less often/with less energy so fewer collisions are successful.

CATALYSTS AND ENZYMES

Section A
1 (a)
2 (c)
3 (d)
4 (d)
5 (c)

Section B
(a) protease
(b) lipase
(c) carbohydrase
(d) isomerase
(e) yeast
2 (a) f
  (b) t
  (c) f
  (d) f
  (e) f

Section C
1 (a) hydrogen peroxide → water + oxygen
  (b) activation energy
  (c) enthalpy change for the reaction
  (d) Path drawn with a lower activation energy.
  (e) increase rate
  (f) no effect

EXOTHERMIC AND ENDOTHERMIC REACTIONS

Section A
1 (a)
2 (c)
3 (d)
4 (c)
5 (b)

Section B
1 (a) Products should be lower in energy than the reactants.
  (b) less
2 (a) Reactants should be lower in energy than the products.
  (b) more

Section C
1 (a) methane + oxygen → carbon dioxide + water vapour
  (b) Energy required to break all the bonds = 2648 kJ per formula mass unit
  Energy given out when bonds are formed = 3466 kJ per formula mass unit
  Energy given out when bonds are formed – Energy required to break all the bonds = 818 kJ per formula mass.
  More energy is given out than taken in, so the reaction is exothermic.

REVERSIBLE REACTIONS

Section A
1 (c)
2 (c)
3 (d)
4 (b)
5 (c)

Section B
1 (a) t
  (b) f
  (c) t
  (d) f
  (e) f
2 (a) decreases the yield
  (b) increases rate
  (c) increases yield

Section C
(a) (i) increases rate
    (ii) no effect
(b) the reaction is reversible/can go backwards or forwards
(c) (i) increase rate
    (ii) decrease yield

THE HABER PROCESS

Section A
1 (b)
2 (d)
3 (b)
4 (d)
5 (c)

Section B
1 decrease yield
2 increase yield
3 increase rate
4 increase rate
5 increase yield
6 no effect
7 increases rate

Section C
1 (a) rate of forward and backwards reactions are equal.
  (b) (i) increase rate
    (ii) decrease yield
  (c) increase yield
  (d) (i) increase rate
    (ii) no effect

RELATIVE FORMULA MASS

Section A
1 (b)
2 (c)
3 (b)
4 (a)
5 (d)

Section B
1 (a) 44
  (b) 18
  (c) 17
  (d) 16
  (e) 32
  (f) 28
2 (a) $\frac{12}{28}$ x 100 = 43%
  (b) $\frac{12}{16}$ x 100 = 75%
  (c) $\frac{24}{28}$ x 100 = 86%

Section C

1 (a) bubbles/ temperature increase/change in mass
  (b) hydrogen
  (c) $\frac{24}{120}$ x 100 = 20%
  (d) $\frac{32}{120}$ x 100 = 27%

RELATIVE FORMULA MASS II

Section A
1 (b)
2 (a)
3 (c)
4 (a)
5 (b)

Section B
1 (a) 2
  (b) 71
  (c) 30
  (d) 28
  (e) 42
  (f) 36.5 (37)
2 (a) $\frac{24}{40}$ x 100 = 60%
  (b) $\frac{24}{95}$ x 100 = 25%
  (c) $\frac{24}{148}$ x 100 = 16%

Section C
1 (a) 0.65/131 and 0.32/16
  1:4 or XeO_4
  (b) empirical formula = XeO_4 molecular formula
  (c) 53/131 and 47/19
  1:6 or XeF_6
  (d) empirical formula = XeF_6 molecular formula
  (e) Noble gases are very unreactive.

BALANCING EQUATIONS

Section A
1 (d) 2 (a) 3 (c) 4 (c)
5 (d)

Section B
1 (a) $2Na + Cl_2 \rightarrow 2NaCl$
  (b) $N_2 + 3H_2 \rightarrow 2NH_3$
  (c) $CH_4 + 2O_2 \rightarrow CO_2 + 2H_2O$
  (d) $2C_2H_6 + 7O_2 \rightarrow 4CO_2 + 6H_2O$

(e) $2C + O_2 \rightarrow 2CO$
(f) $C + CO_2 \rightarrow 2CO$
(g) $2Mg + O_2 \rightarrow 2MgO$
(h) $2H_2 + O_2 \rightarrow 2H_2O$
(i) $H_2 + I_2 \rightarrow 2HI$
(j) $H_2 + Cl_2 \rightarrow 2HCl$
(k) $2KI + Cl_2 \rightarrow 2KCl + I_2$
(l) $2Ca + O_2 \rightarrow 2CaO$
(m) $H_2 + Br_2 \rightarrow 2HBr$
(n) $2K + I_2 \rightarrow 2KI$
                    (14 marks)

Section C
(a) Carbon dioxide gas is produced.
(b) (i) 1
    (ii) 1
    (iii) 3
(c) $CaCO_{3(s)} + 2HCl_{(aq)} \rightarrow CaCl_{2(aq)} + H_2O_{(g)} + CO_{2(g)}$

CALCULATING MASSES

Section A
1 (b)
2 (c)
3 (b)
4 (b)
5 (a)

Section B
1 (a) $48 \, dm^3$
  (b) $12 \, dm^3$
  (c) $6 \, dm^3$
  (d) $72 \, dm^3$
  (e) $24 \, dm^3$
2 (a) 60 g
  (b) 48 g

Section C
(a) 100
(b) 40%
(c) (i) 2.2 g
    (ii) 5.6 g

ELECTROLYSIS

Section A
1 (b)
2 (a)
3 (b)
4 (d)
5 (a)   (5 marks)

Section B

1 positive electrode = (a)
  positive ion = (e)
  bromine gas = (b)
  negative electrode = (c)
  negative ion = (f)
  potassium metal = (d)
2 (a) 3.2g
  (b) 0.48 dm³/litres

Section C

(a) 2 bromine ions give
   up an electron each
   or two electrons to
   form a bromine
   molecule

(b) $Pb^{2+}_{(l)} + 2e^- \rightarrow Pb_{(l)}$

(c) Each lead ion gains
   two electrons to
   from a lead atom

TYPES OF REACTION

Section A

1 (c)
2 (d)
3 (d)
4 (b)
5 (c)

Section B

neutralisation, water,
sodium
chloride, given out
exothermic

Section C

1 (a) bubbles/increase in
    temperature/decreas
    e in mass
  (b) neutralisation
    /exothermic
  (c) exothermic

(d) calcium carbonate
  + hydrochloric acid
  → calcium chloride
  + water + carbon
  dioxide
(e) $CaCO_{3(s)} + 2HCl_{(aq)} \rightarrow CaCl_{2(aq)} + CO_{2(g)} + H_2O_{(l)}$

LETTS EDUCATIONAL
The Chiswick Centre
414 Chiswick High Road
London W4 5TF
Tel: 020 8996 3333
Fax: 020 8742 8390
Email: mail@lettsed.co.uk
Website: www.letts-education.com

C **This is a GCSE-style question. Answer all parts of the questions**

1 Magnesium reacts with oxygen to form the compound magnesium oxide.
The dot and cross diagrams of magnesium and oxygen atoms are shown below.
Only the outer electron shell is shown.

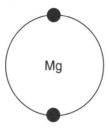 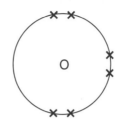

This compound is held together by ionic bonds. These bonds occur between oppositely charged Mg^{2+} and O^{2-} ions.

A magnesium ion, Mg^{2+} is formed when a magnesium atom loses two electrons.

(a) Show the arrangement of electrons in a magnesium ion.

(1 mark)

(b) An oxide, O^{2-} ion is formed from an oxygen atom during the reaction.
Show the arrangement of electrons in an oxide ion.

(1 mark)

Score   /2

How well did you do?

1–4 Try again
5–7 Getting there
8–10 Good work
11–13 Excellent!

TOTAL SCORE   /13

For more on this topic
see page 50 of your Success Guide

IONIC AND COVALENT COMPOUNDS

A Choose just one answer, a, b, c or d.

1 Which of these substances is not a simple molecule?
(a) chlorine   (c) graphite
(b) oxygen   (d) water   (1 mark)

2 Which of these statements is true of graphite?
(a) It dissolves in water.
(b) It conducts electricity.
(c) It is white.
(d) All the atoms in graphite are held together by strong ionic bonds.   (1 mark)

3 Which of these compounds forms molecules?
(a) sodium chloride
(b) potassium bromide
(c) magnesium oxide
(d) hydrogen chloride   (1 mark)

4 Which of these statements is true of ionic compounds?
(a) They dissolve in water.
(b) They do not conduct electricity when molten.
(c) They have low melting points.
(d) They contain bonds which involve a shared pair of electrons.   (1 mark)

5 Which of these types of structure do ionic compounds form?
(a) giant ionic structure
(b) molecules
(c) metallic
(d) giant covalent structure   (1 mark)

Score /5

B Answer all parts of the question.

1 Carbon can form in two forms, diamond and graphite. This diagram shows the arrangement of carbon atoms in diamond.

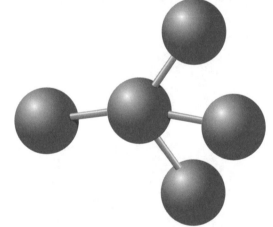

(a) Draw the arrangement of carbon atoms in graphite.

(2 marks)

(b) Explain the type of bonding in the two forms of carbon, diamond and graphite.

(i) diamond

_____

(ii) graphite

_____
(2 marks)

Score /4

C This is a GCSE-style question. Answer all parts of the question.

1 Hydrogen and oxygen atoms can join together to form the covalent compound water, H_2O.
The reaction can be represented by the symbol equation

$2H_{2(g)} + O_{2(g)} \rightarrow 2H_2O_{(g)}$

(a) Choose words from the list below to complete the following sentences.

| electrons | molecule | neutrons | protons | one | two |

Each water .... consists of two hydrogen atoms and ....

oxygen atom. These atoms are held together by shared pairs of ....

(3 marks)

(b) Draw the electron arrangement in one molecule of water. (You need only draw the outer electron shells.)

(2 marks)

(c) Water boils at 100 °C. Explain why water has quite a low boiling point.

....

.... (2 marks)

Score   /7

How well did you do?

1–5   Try again
6–10   Getting there
11–13 Good work
14–16 Excellent!

TOTAL SCORE   /16

For more on this topic
see page 52 of your Success Guide

THE PERIODIC TABLE

A — Choose just one answer, a, b, c or d.

1 Which of these elements is the odd one out?
(a) lithium
(b) sodium
(c) bromine
(d) potassium (1 mark)

2 Which of these elements is the odd one out?
(a) chlorine
(b) sodium
(c) bromine
(d) iodine (1 mark)

3 How many electrons are in the outer shell of all Group II atoms?
(a) 0
(b) 1
(c) 2
(d) 3 (1 mark)

4 What is the name given to the horizontal rows in the periodic table?
(a) groups
(b) periods
(c) sections
(d) columns (1 mark)

5 On what did Mendeleev base his periodic table?
(a) increasing atomic mass
(b) colour
(c) increasing number of neutrons
(d) alphabetical order (1 mark)

Score /5

B — Answer all parts of the questions.

1 Cross out the incorrect word or phrase in each sentence.

(a) In the modern periodic table the elements are arranged in order of increasing atomic/mass number.

(b) The vertical columns in the periodic table are called groups/periods.

(c) Elements in the same row of the periodic table have the same number of electron shells/outer electron structure.

(d) If an atom has three electrons in its outer shell it is in Group V/III.

(e) Beryllium, magnesium, calcium, strontium and barium are all members of Group II/period 2.
(5 marks)

2 Mendeleev ordered the elements in his periodic table according to their atomic masses. Describe the two big decisions that Mendeleev made.

....
.... (2 marks)

3 Why did Mendeleev not include the element germanium in his periodic table?

.... (1 mark)

Score /7

These are GCSE-style questions. Answer all parts of the questions.

1 Dimitri Mendeleev arranged the elements into order based on their atomic masses. The diagram below shows part of Mendeleev's arrangement.

Group

III	IV	V	VI	VII
11 **B** Boron	12 **C** Carbon	14 **N** Nitrogen	16 **O** Oxygen	19 **F** Fluorine
27 **Al** Aluminium	28 **Si** Silicon	31 **P** Phosphorus	32 **S** Sulphur	35.5 **Cl** Chlorine
		75 **As** Arsenic	79 **Se** Selenium	80 **Br** Bromine
115 **In** Indium	119 **Sn** Tin	122 **Sb** Antimony		

(a) Why are the Noble gases not shown in Mendeleev's table?

.... (1 mark)

(b) The next two elements are iodine and tellurium.

Iodine has a mass number of 127, while tellurium has a mass of 128. If the elements in the periodic table were to be arranged just on their atomic masses, into which group should iodine and tellurium be placed?

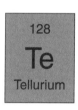

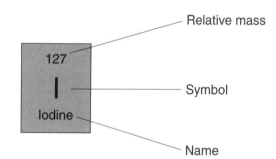

Relative mass

Symbol

Name

(i) tellurium ....

(ii) iodine .... (2 marks)

(c) Explain why Mendeleev actually swapped the order of iodine and tellurium.

.... (1 mark)

(d) Explain how the elements are now arranged in the modern periodic table.

.... (1 mark)

Score   /5

How well did you do?

1–5   Try again
6–10   Getting there
11–14 Good work
15–17 Excellent!

TOTAL SCORE   /17

For more on this topic
see page 54 of your Success Guide

TRANSITION METALS

A

Choose just one answer, a, b, c or d.

1 Which of these transition metals rusts?
(a) copper   (c) nickel
(b) iron   (d) platinum   (1 mark)

2 Which of these transition metals is used in the Haber process to make ammonia?
(a) copper
(b) iron
(c) nickel
(d) platinum   (1 mark)

3 Which of these transition metals is used as a catalyst in the production of margarine?
(a) copper
(b) iron
(c) nickel
(d) platinum   (1 mark)

4 Which of these transition metals can be made into steel?
(a) copper
(b) iron
(c) nickel
(d) platinum   (1 mark)

5 Which of these transition metals is used to make electrical wires?
(a) copper
(b) iron
(c) nickel
(d) platinum   (1 mark)

Score /5

B

Answer all parts of the question.

1 (a) Draw the arrangement of particles in metals.

(2 marks)

(b) What is meant by the term a 'free' electron?

.... (1 mark)

(c) Give a property which is typical of metals. For the property you have chosen, explain how the arrangement of particles causes the property.

....

.... (2 marks)

Score /5

C **These are GCSE-style questions. Answer all parts of the questions.**

1 Use the words in the box to complete the sentences below.

pottery glazes	ionic	catalysts	iron	white	colourless	transition

Group I metals react with non-metals to form ....compounds.

These compounds are .... solids which dissolve in water to form

.... solutions.

Most .... metals form coloured compounds.

The different colours of transition metal compounds means that they can be used

as ....

Many transition metals are also good .... The metal .... is used
industrially in the manufacture of ammonia. **(7 marks)**

2 Match each transition metal to its property and its use.

Metal	Property	Use
IRON	Good conductor of heat	Coins
NICKEL	Strong	Saucepans
COPPER	Hardwearing	Bridges

(3 marks)

3 These are all properties of transition metals. Match each property to its meaning.

Property	Meaning
Strong	An electrical current can easily pass through them.
High melting point	They can support heavy loads.
Good conductor of electricity	They do not form liquids until they are very hot.

(3 marks)

Score /13

How well did you do?
1–7 Try again
8–12 Getting there
13–18 Good work
19–23 Excellent!

TOTAL SCORE /23

**For more on this topic
see page 56 of your Success Guide**

THE ALKALI METALS

STRUCTURE AND BONDING

A Choose just one answer, a, b, c or d.

1 Which is the odd one out?
(a) lithium   (c) potassium
(b) bromine   (d) sodium   (1 mark)

2 Name the gas given off when a metal reacts with water.
(a) oxygen
(b) helium
(c) hydrogen
(d) carbon dioxide   (1 mark)

3 What is the test for the gas hydrogen?
(a) relights a glowing splint.
(b) bleaches damp litmus paper
(c) burns with a squeaky pop
(d) turns limewater cloudy   (1 mark)

4 What are the products made when sodium reacts with water?
(a) sodium + water
(b) sodium hydroxide + water
(c) sodium hydroxide + hydrogen
(d) water + hydrogen   (1 mark)

5 Which of these statements is not true of Group I metals?
(a) Down the group they become more reactive.
(b) Down the group their melting points decrease.
(c) Down the group their boiling points decrease.
(d) They react with non-metals to form coloured compounds.   (1 mark)

Score   /5

B Answer all parts of the questions.

1 True or false?

	True	False
(a) Lithium, sodium and potassium are more dense than water.	☐	☐
(b) Potassium burns with a lilac flame.	☐	☐
(c) All atoms of alkali metals have one electron in their outer shell.	☐	☐
(d) Universal Indicator will turn purple in sodium hydroxide solution.	☐	☐
(e) Alkali metals become more reactive down the Group.	☐	☐ (5 marks)

2 Complete the following word and symbol equations

(a) lithium + water → .... + hydrogen

(b) $2Li(s) + 2H_2O(l) \rightarrow 2LiOH(aq) +$ ....(g)

(c) sodium + ... → sodium hydroxide + hydrogen

(d) ....(s) $+ 2H_2O(l) \rightarrow 2NaOH(aq) +$ ....(g)

(e) potassium + water → potassium hydroxide + ...

(f) ....(s) $+ 2H_2O(l) \rightarrow 2KOH(aq) + H_2(g)$ (7 marks

)

Score   /12

56

C This is a GCSE-style question. Answer all parts of the question.

1 Group I of the periodic table includes the metals lithium, sodium, potassium and rubidium. The diagram below shows a science teacher placing a piece of sodium metal into a bowl of water.

Safety screen

Water trough

SODIUM

The Group I metals
Lithium
Sodium
Potassium
Rubidium

(a) The reaction between sodium and water can be represented using a word equation. Complete the word equation below.

Sodium + water ➜ .... + ...   (2 marks)

(b) After the reaction had finished, the scientist added some Universal Indicator.

(i) What colour did the Universal Indicator turn? .... (1 mark)

(ii) What does this show has been made?

.... (1 mark)

(c) Potassium also reacts with cold water in a similar way to sodium.

(i) Why do sodium and potassium react in a similar way? Explain your answer in terms of the electron structure of sodium and potassium atoms.

....

.... (1 mark)

(ii) Will sodium or potassium react more vigorously? Explain your answer in terms of the electron structure of sodium and potassium atoms.

....

.... (2 marks)

Score   /7

How well did you do?
1–7   Try again
8–12   Getting there
13–18   Good work
19–24   Excellent!

TOTAL SCORE   /24

For more on this topic
see page 58 of your Success Guide

THE HALOGENS

A

Choose just one answer, a, b, c or d.

1 Which halogen is a pale yellow gas?
(a) fluorine   (c) bromine
(b) chlorine   (d) iodine   (1 mark)

2 Which halogen is the only non-metal element that is a liquid at room temperature?
(a) fluorine
(b) chlorine
(c) bromine
(d) iodine   (1 mark)

3 A solution of which halogen can be used as an antiseptic?
(a) fluorine
(b) chlorine
(c) bromine
(d) iodine   (1 mark)

4 Which halogen is used in water purification?
(a) fluorine
(b) chlorine
(c) bromine
(d) iodine   (1 mark)

5 Which halogen has the smallest atoms?
(a) fluorine
(b) chlorine
(c) bromine
(d) iodine   (1 mark)

Score   /5

B

Answer all parts of the questions.

1 True or false?

                                                                                True   False

(a) The melting points and boiling points of halogens decrease down the Group. ☐ ☐

(b) Halogens are safe for young children to use. ☐ ☐

(c) Halogens do not conduct electricity when molten. ☐ ☐

(d) Halogens are colourless gases. ☐ ☐

(e) Chlorine forms compounds in which the chloride ion has a 1⁻ charge. ☐ ☐   (5 marks)

2 Complete these word and symbol equations   (7 marks)

(a) chlorine + potassium iodide → .... + ...

(b) $Cl_2 + 2KI \rightarrow$ .... $+ I_2$

(c) chlorine + potassium bromide → .... + ...

(d) $Cl_2 + 2KBr \rightarrow$ .... + ...

Score   /12

58

C This is a GCSE-style question. Answer all parts of the question.

1 The diagram below shows Group VII of the periodic table.

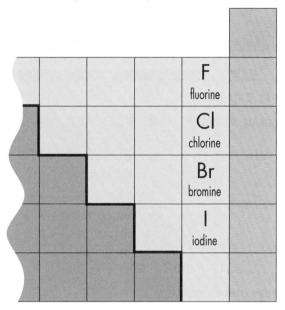

Group VII	
Symbol	**Element**
F	fluorine
Cl	chlorine
Br	bromine
I	iodine

(a) Give one use of the halogen, chlorine.

.... (1 mark)

(b) Explain the trend in reactivity in the Group VII elements.

....

.... (2 marks)

(c) If chlorine gas is bubbled through a solution of potassium iodide, a displacement reaction occurs and potassium chloride and iodine are produced.

(i) Write a word equation to represent this reaction.

.... (1 mark)

(ii) This reaction can also be represented using a symbol equation. Balance the equation below to show this reaction. (1 mark)

........$KI_{(aq)}$ + ...$Cl_{2(g)}$ → ....$KCl_{(aq)}$ + ...$I_{2(g)}$

Score   /5

How well did you do?

1–7   Try again
8–12   Getting there
13–18   Good work
19–22   Excellent!

TOTAL SCORE   /22

For more on this topic
see page 60 of your Success Guide

59

NOBLE GASES

A

Choose just one answer, a, b, c or d.

1 Which is the most unreactive group found in the periodic table?
(a) Group I   (c) Group VII
(b) Group II   (d) Group 0   (1 mark)

2 What does monatomic mean?
(a) individual atoms
(b) one colour
(c) one outer electron
(d) they are colourless   (1 mark)

3 How many electrons do Noble gas atoms need to gain to get a full outer shell?
(a) 1
(b) 2
(c) 7
(d) 0   (1 mark)

4 Which Noble gas is used in light bulbs?
(a) helium
(b) neon
(c) krypton
(d) argon   (1 mark)

5 Which Noble gas is used in air balloons?
(a) helium
(b) neon
(c) krypton
(d) argon   (1 mark)

Chemistry

Score   /5

B

Answer all parts of the questions.

1 Draw the electron structure of an atom of helium and of neon.

(You need only draw the outer shell of electrons.)

(2 marks)

2 Delete the incorrect word or phrase in the following sentences.

(a) The Noble gases all have a full electron/proton shell.

(b) This means they do/do not react.

(c) The density of Noble gases decreases/increases down the group.

(d) The boiling points of Noble gases decrease/increase down the group.

(e) Noble gases are monatomic/diatomic.

(f) Noble gases are colourless/ green.

(6 marks)

Score   /8

C **These are GCSE-style questions. Answer all parts of the questions.**

1 Xenon is found in Group 0 of the periodic table. It is a very unreactive gas.

Explain why xenon is such an unreactive gas.

....

.... (2 marks)

2 Shade the area of the periodic table which shows where the Noble gases are found. (1 mark)

3 Give a use of the Noble gas, helium.

.... (1 mark)

4 The diagram below shows the outer structure of chlorine, Cl, and of argon, Ar.
X represents an electron.

Cl

Ar

Explain why chlorine is found as chlorine molecules, Cl_2, but argon never forms molecules.

....

.... (2 marks)

Score /6

How well did you do?

1–5 Try again
6–10 Getting there
11–14 Good work
15–19 Excellent!

TOTAL SCORE /19

**For more on this topic
see page 62 of your Success Guide**

ELECTROLYSIS OF BRINE

A Choose just one answer, a, b, c or d.

1 What is chlorine used to make?
(a) salt
(b) soap
(c) bleach
(d) margarine   (1 mark)

2 What is hydrogen used to make?
(a) salt
(b) soap
(c) bleach
(d) margarine   (1 mark)

3 What is sodium hydroxide used to make?
(a) salt
(b) soap
(c) copper
(d) margarine   (1 mark)

4 During the electrolysis of sodium chloride solution, what is the name of the gas released at the positive electrode?
(a) sodium hydroxide
(b) hydrogen
(c) chlorine
(d) sodium   (1 mark)

5 During the electrolysis of sodium chloride solution, what is the name of the gas released at the negative electrode?
(a) sodium hydroxide
(b) hydrogen
(c) chlorine
(d) sodium   (1 mark)

Score   /5

B Answer all parts of the questions.

1 Use the diagrams in the box to label the diagram below.

Sodium hydroxide solution

Negative electrode

Positive electrode

Hydrogen gas

Chlorine gas

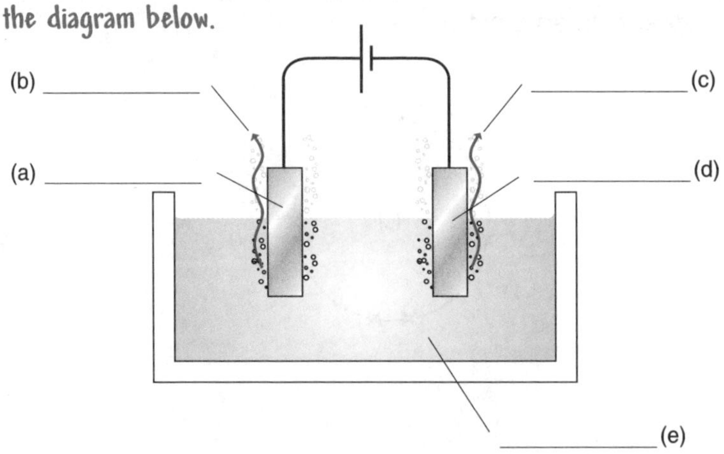

(b) _____   (c) _____
(a) _____   (d) _____
_____ (e)

(5 marks)

2 True or false?

	True	False
(a) Sodium chloride solution is called brine.	☐	☐
(b) Hydrogen is made in the manufacture of butter.	☐	☐
(c) Chlorine is used in the manufacture of the plastic PVC.	☐	☐
(d) Sodium is a transition metal.	☐	☐
(e) Chlorine is a Group VII gas.	☐	☐

(5 marks)

Score   /10

C This is a GCSE-style question. Answer all parts of the question.

1 The diagram below shows the electrolysis of concentrated sodium chloride solution.

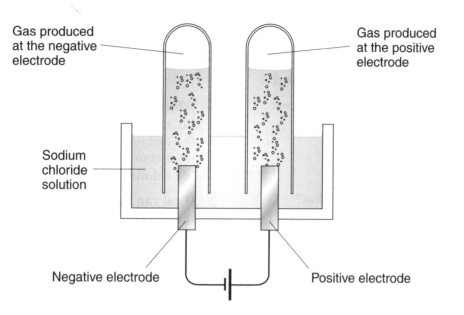

Gas produced at the negative electrode

Gas produced at the positive electrode

Sodium chloride solution

Negative electrode

Positive electrode

(a) Name the gas produced at the positive electrode.

.... (1 mark)

(b) Give the equation for the reaction that occurs at the positive electrode.

.... (1 mark)

(c) Give one use of this gas.

.... (1 mark)

(d) Name the gas produced at the negative electrode.

.... (1 mark)

(e) Give the equation for the reaction that occurs at the negative electrode.

.... (1 mark)

(f) Give one use of this gas.

.... (1 mark)

(g) Name the other chemical made in this reaction.

.... (1 mark)

(h) Give one use of this chemical.

.... (1 mark)

Score   /8

How well did you do?

1–7   Try again
8–12   Getting there
13–18 Good work
19–23 Excellent!

TOTAL SCORE   /23

For more on this topic
see page 64 of your Success Guide

COMMON TESTS AND SAFETY HAZARDS

A

Choose just one answer, a, b, c or d.

1 Which gas bleaches damp litmus paper?
(a) oxygen
(b) carbon dioxide
(c) hydrogen
(d) chlorine   (1 mark)

2 Which gas relights a glowing splint?
(a) oxygen
(b) carbon dioxide
(c) hydrogen
(d) chlorine   (1 mark)

3 Which gas burns with a squeaky pop?
(a) oxygen
(b) carbon dioxide
(c) hydrogen
(d) chlorine   (1 mark)

4 Which gas will turn limewater cloudy?
(a) oxygen
(b) carbon dioxide
(c) hydrogen
(d) chlorine   (1 mark)

5 What can bromine water be used to test for?
(a) alkenes
(b) oxygen
(c) hydrogen
(d) nitrogen   (1 mark)

Sulphuric Acid

Alcohol

Score   /5

B

Answer all parts of the question.

1 Complete the following the sentences.

Carbon dioxide

Limewater is used to test for the gas .... The gas is .... through the limewater. If the limewater turns .... the gas is carbon dioxide.

Hydrogen

The gas hydrogen is tested for using a .... splint. If hydrogen is present it will burn with a ....

Oxygen

The gas .... is needed for things to burn. Things burn more brightly in pure oxygen than they do in ....

If a .... splint is placed in a test tube containing oxygen, the splint .... (9 marks)

Score   /9

64

These are GCSE-style questions. Answer all parts of the questions.

1 Some chemicals are dangerous and should only be used with great care. Containers holding these chemicals are marked with a label, which gives information about that chemical. Below are four hazard symbols and four hazard descriptions. Draw a line to connect each symbol to the correct description.

(4 marks)

Hazard symbols

 (a)

 (b)

 (c)

 (d)

Description of hazard

Corrosive

Attacks and destroys living tissues including eyes and skin.

Harmful

Similar to toxic, but less dangerous.

Highly flammable

Catches fire easily.

Toxic

Can cause death if swallowed, breathed in or absorbed through the skin.

2 A student carries out an experiment on an unknown compound. The compound is a bright pink colour. This means that the compound contains the transition metal cobalt. The student believes that the compound could be cobalt chloride. When cobalt chloride is heated fiercely, it gives off the gas chlorine. Explain how the student should test the gas given off when the compound is heated to see if it is chlorine.

....

....

....

....

....

....

....

(2 marks)

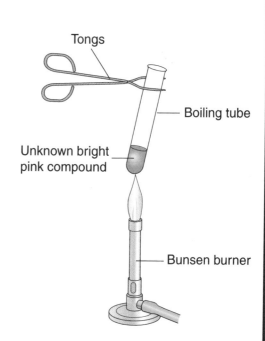

Tongs

Boiling tube

Unknown bright pink compound

Bunsen burner

Score   /6

COMMON TESTS AND SAFETY HAZARDS

How well did you do?

1–5   Try again
6–11   Getting there
12–15 Good work
16–20 Excellent!

TOTAL SCORE   /20

For more on this topic see page 68 of your Success Guide

RATES OF REACTION

A

Choose just one answer, a, b, c or d.

1 **What does a catalyst do?**
(a) It increases the rate of reaction.
(b) It increases the temperature.
(c) It increases the yield.
(d) It increases the time needed for the reaction. **(1 mark)**

2 **How can the rate of reaction be measured?**
(a) Measure the temperature.
(b) Look at the equation.
(c) Reduce the temperature.
(d) Measure how fast the products are made. **(1 mark)**

3 **Which of these will *not* increase the rate of reaction?**
(a) adding a catalyst
(b) decreasing the temperature

(c) increasing the surface area
(d) increasing the concentration **(1 mark)**

4 **Which of these will *not* decrease the rate of reaction?**
(a) adding a catalyst
(b) decreasing the temperature
(c) decreasing the surface area
(d) decreasing the concentration **(1 mark)**

5 **When is the rate of a reaction normally fastest?**
(a) 0–10 s
(b) 10–20 s
(c) 20–30 s
(d) after 30 minutes **(1 mark)**

Score   /5

B

Answer all parts of the question.

1 George is investigating the rate of reaction between hydrochloric acid and calcium carbonate. The reaction can be represented by the equation

hydrochloric acid + calcium carbonate → calcium chloride + water + carbon dioxide

He recorded the volume of carbon dioxide gas produced every 10 seconds in the table below.

Time (s)	0	10	20	30	40	50	60	70	80	90	100
Volume of gas made (cm^3)	0	30	40	50	56	60	60	60	60	60	60

(a) Draw a graph to show the results of George's experiment on graph paper. **(3 marks)**

(b) When is the rate of the reaction fastest?

.... **(1 mark)**

(c) When has the reaction finished?

.... **(1 mark)**

Score   /5

C **This is a GCSE-style question. Answer all parts of the question.**

1 The reaction between magnesium and sulphuric acid can be represented by the word equation

magnesium + sulphuric acid → magnesium sulphate + hydrogen

A student wants to investigate the rate of this reaction. He sets up some equipment, which is shown in the diagram below.

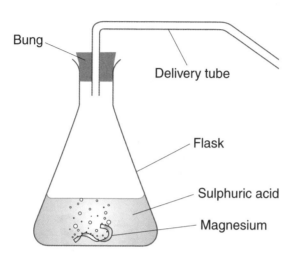

Bung

Delivery tube

Flask

Sulphuric acid

Magnesium

(a) Complete the diagram to show how the amount of hydrogen gas produced can be measured.

(2 marks)

(b) What other piece of equipment will the student need to investigate the rate of this reaction?

.... (1 mark)

(c) What measurements should the student take?

.... (1 mark)

(d) The student carries out the reaction at two different temperatures, 40 °C and 20 °C.

(i) At which of these temperatures will the rate of the reaction be slowest?

.... (1 mark)

(ii) Explain why the rate of the reaction is slower at the temperature you have chosen.

....

....

....

.... (3 marks)

Score   /8

How well did you do?

1–5   Try again
6–10   Getting there
11–14   Good work
15–18   Excellent!

TOTAL SCORE   /18

For more on this topic
see page 70 of your Success Guide

CATALYSTS AND ENZYMES

A

Choose just one answer, a, b, c or d.

1 What does the catalyst isomerase do?
 (a) It converts glucose to fructose.
 (b) It converts fructose to glucose.
 (c) It breaks down proteins.
 (d) It breaks down fats. (1 mark)

2 What does the enzyme protease do?
 (a) It converts glucose to fructose.
 (b) It converts fructose to glucose.
 (c) It breaks down proteins.
 (d) It breaks down fats. (1 mark)

3 What does the enzyme lipase do?
 (a) It converts glucose to fructose.
 (b) It converts fructose to glucose.
 (c) It breaks down proteins.
 (d) It breaks down fats. (1 mark)

4 What is added to milk to make yoghurt?
 (a) lactose
 (b) fructose
 (c) yeast
 (d) bacteria (1 mark)

5 What is glucose?
 (a) a type of fat
 (b) a type of protein
 (c) a type of sugar
 (d) a type of enzyme (1 mark)

Score /5

B

Answer all parts of the questions.

1 Add the correct catalyst for each job to complete the table below.

Job that it does	Catalyst
(a) Breaks down proteins	
(b) Breaks down fats	
(c) Breaks down starch into sugar	
(d) Converts glucose to fructose	
(e) Converts sugar into alcohol	

(5 marks)

2 True or false?

	True	False
(a) Catalysts increase the yield of a reaction.	☐	☐
(b) Catalysts can be used many times.	☐	☐
(c) A catalysed reaction will have higher activation energy than the uncatalysed reaction.	☐	☐
(d) Most enzymes work best at very low temperatures.	☐	☐
(e) All enzymes work best in neutral conditions.	☐	☐

(5 marks)

Score /10

C

This is a GCSE-style question. Answer all parts of the question.

1 The chemical hydrogen peroxide breaks down to form water and oxygen. The symbol diagram for this reaction is shown below.

$$2H_2O_{2(l)} \rightarrow 2H_2O_{(l)} + O_{2(g)}$$

(a) Write a word equation to represent this reaction.

.... (1 mark)

The energy level diagram for this reaction is shown below.

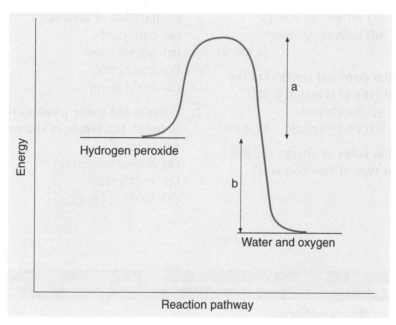

(b) Explain what energy change 'a' represents on the graph.

.... (1 mark)

(c) Explain what energy change 'b' represents on the graph.

.... (1 mark)

This reaction can be catalysed by a black powder called manganese dioxide.

(d) Draw on to your graph the reaction pathway for the catalysed reaction.

.... (1 mark)

(e) How will the catalyst affect the rate of this reaction?

.... (1 mark)

(f) How will the catalyst affect the yield of this reaction?

.... (1 mark)

Score   /6

How well did you do?

1–5   Try again
6–11   Getting there
12–16   Good work
17–21   Excellent!

TOTAL SCORE   /21

For more on this topic
see page 72 of your Success Guide

EXOTHERMIC AND ENDOTHERMIC REACTIONS

A Choose just one answer, a, b, c or d.

1 The amount of energy that must be taken in to break one mole of bonds is the
(a) bond energy   (c) formation energy
(b) rate   (d) activation energy
(1 mark)

2 If, overall, a reaction gives out energy (in the form of heat), what type of reaction is it?
(a) catalysed   (c) exothermic
(b) uncatalysed   (d) endothermic   (1 mark)

3 If, overall, a reaction takes in energy (in the form of heat), what type of reaction is it?
(a) catalysed
(b) uncatalysed
(c) exothermic
(d) endothermic   (1 mark)

4 Methane is the gas burnt in Bunsen burners. Which of these reactions best describes the combustion of methane?
(a) catalysed
(b) uncatalysed
(c) exothermic
(d) endothermic   (1 mark)

5 What is the name given to the energy required to break the bonds in the reactants?
(a) take off
(b) activation energy
(c) exothermic
(d) starting energy   (1 mark)

Score   /5

B Answer all parts of the questions.

1 (a) Draw an energy level diagram for an exothermic reaction.

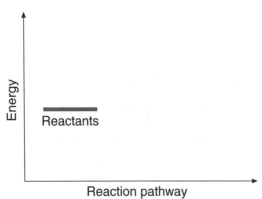

(b) Delete the incorrect word in this sentence:

In exothermic reactions the products have more/less energy than the reactants.

2 (a) Draw the energy level diagram for an endothermic reaction.

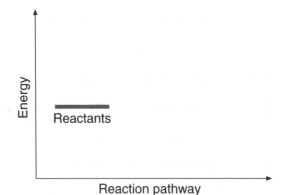

(b) Delete the incorrect word in this sentence:

In endothermic reactions the products have more/less energy than the reactants.

Score   /4

This is a GCSE-style question. Answer all parts of the question.

1 Methane is used as a fuel in Bunsen burners. Fuels are substances that can be burnt to release heat energy. When methane is completely burnt in oxygen, carbon dioxide and water vapour are produced.

The symbol equation for this reaction is shown below.

$$CH_{4(g)} + 2O_{2(g)} \rightarrow CO_{2(g)} + 2H_2O_{(g)}$$

(a) Write a word equation to represent this reaction.

.... (1 mark)

The diagram below shows the bonds present in molecules of methane, oxygen, carbon dioxide and water vapour.

Bond energy* (kJ per formula mass)	Bond
413	C–H
498	O=O
805	C=O
464	O–H

*The bond energy is the amount of energy released when the bond is formed or taken in when the bond is broken.

(b) Use the diagrams and bond energies above to prove that the burning of methane is an exothermic reaction.

....

....

.... (4 marks)

Score   /5

How well did you do?

1–4   Try again
5–7   Getting there
8–11   Good work
12–14   Excellent!

TOTAL SCORE   /14

For more on this topic
see page 74 of your Success Guide

REVERSIBLE REACTIONS

A

Choose just one answer, a, b, c or d.

1 In a reversible reaction, the forward reaction is exothermic, what can be said about the reverse reaction?
(**a**) It is faster.　　　　(**c**) It is endothermic.
(**b** It is more colourful.　(**d**) It is more useful.
(1 mark)

2 In a reaction, energy in the form of heat is given out. How can this reaction be best described?
(**a**) fast　　　　(**c**) exothermic
(**b**) slow　　　　(**d**) endothermic　(1 mark)

3 In a reaction, energy in the form of heat is taken in. How can this reaction be best described?
(**a**) fast　　　　(**c**) exothermic
(**b**) slow　　　　(**d**) endothermic　(1 mark)

4 In a reaction, three gas molecules join together to form two new gas molecules. If the pressure is increased, what will happen to the yield of the products?
(**a**) stay the same　(**d**) You can only tell by
(**b**) increase　　　　　doing the experiments.
(**c**) decrease　　　　　　　　　　(1 mark)

5 In a reaction, one gas molecule breaks down to form two new gas molecules. If the pressure is increased, what will happen to the yield of the products?
(**a**) stay the same　(**d**) You can only tell by
(**b**) increase　　　　　doing the experiments.
(**c**) decrease　　　　　　　　　　(1 mark)

Score　/5

B

Answer all parts of the questions.

1 True or false?

	True	False
(a) In a closed system nothing can escape.	☐	☐
(b) If, during an exothermic reaction, the temperature is increased, the yield increases.	☐	☐
(c) If, during an exothermic reaction, the temperature is increased, the rate of reaction increases.	☐	☐
(d) Forward reactions are always exothermic.	☐	☐
(e) Increasing the pressure always increases the yield of a reaction.	☐	☐

(5 marks)

2 In a reversible reaction $A + B \rightleftharpoons C$.
A, B and C are all gases. The forward reaction is exothermic.
Describe the effect for each of these situations.

(a) increasing the temperature on the yield. ....

....

(b) increasing the temperature on the rate of the reaction. ....

....

(c) increasing pressure on the yield. ....

.... (3 marks)

Score　/8

C

This is a GCSE-style question. Answer all parts of the question.

1 Sulphuric acid is a very widely used chemical. Sulphuric acid is made from a compound called sulphur trioxide. Sulphur trioxide is made by the contact process.

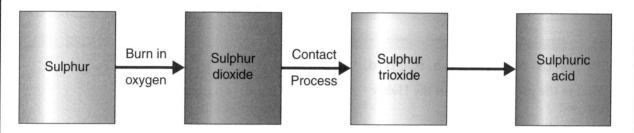

During the contact process sulphur dioxide reacts with oxygen to form sulphur trioxide. This reaction can be represented by the symbol equation below.

Sulphur dioxide + oxygen $\rightleftharpoons$ sulphur trioxide

$$2SO_{2(g)} + O_{2(g)} \rightleftharpoons 2SO_{3(g)}$$

This is an exothermic reaction.

The reaction is carried out in the presence of a vanadium oxide catalyst.

(a) What effect does the catalyst have on

   (i) the rate of reaction?

   .... (1 mark)

   (ii) the yield of sulphur trioxide?

   .... (1 mark)

(b) Explain what the symbol $\rightleftharpoons$ means.

   .... (1 mark)

(c) Industrially, this reaction is carried out at 450 °C. What would be the effect of increasing this temperature on

   (i) the rate of reaction?

   .... (1 mark)

   (ii) the yield of sulphur trioxide?

   .... (1 mark)

Score   /5

REVERSIBLE REACTIONS

w well did you do?

  1–5 Try again
  6–10 Getting there
11–14 Good work
15–18 Excellent!

TOTAL SCORE   **/18**

For more on this topic see page 76 of your Success Guide

THE HABER PROCESS

A Choose just one answer, a, b, c or d.

1 What is the pressure used in the Haber process?
(a) 100 atmospheres
(b) 200 atmospheres
(c) 300 atmospheres
(d) 400 atmospheres   (1 mark)

2 What is the temperature used in the Haber process?
(a) 150 degrees Celsius
(b) 250 degrees Celsius
(c) 350 degrees Celsius
(d) 450 degrees Celsius   (1 mark)

3 What is the catalyst used in the Haber process?
(a) copper   (c) nickel
(b) iron   (d) platinum   (1 mark)

4 What does a catalyst do?
(a) increases the temperature
(b) increases the pressure
(c) increases the yield
(d) increases the rate   (1 mark)

5 Where is the nitrogen used in the Haber process obtained from?
(a) natural gas   (c) air
(b) ammonia   (d) volcanoes   (1 mark)

Score   /5

B Answer all parts of the questions.

1 What is the effect of increasing the temperature on the yield of an exothermic reaction?
.... (1 mark)

2 What is the effect of increasing the temperature on the yield of an endothermic reaction?
.... (1 mark)

3 What is the effect of increasing the temperature on the rate of an exothermic reaction?
.... (1 mark)

4 What is the effect of increasing the temperature on the rate of an endothermic reaction?
.... (1 mark)

5 In a reaction, four reactant molecules form just two product molecules. What is the effect of increasing the pressure on the yield of this reaction?
.... (1 mark)

6 What is the effect of adding a catalyst on the yield of a reaction?
.... (1 mark)

7 What is the effect of adding a catalyst on the rate of a reaction?
.... (1 mark)

Score   /7

This is a GCSE-style question. Answer all parts of the question.

1 Ammonia is made industrially using the Haber process. Ammonia is an important chemical, which is used in the manufacture of fertilisers.

The reaction between hydrogen and nitrogen to make ammonia is shown by the symbol equation below.

$$N_{2(g)} + 3H_{2(g)} \rightleftharpoons 2NH_{3(g)}$$

The forward reaction is exothermic.
In a closed system, where nothing can enter or leave, the reaction will eventually reach an equilibrium.

(a) What is meant by the term equilibrium?

.... (1 mark)

(b) The process is carried out at a temperature of 450 °C. If the temperature is increased, what effect will this have on

(i) the rate of this reaction

.... (1 mark)

(ii) the yield of this reaction

.... (1 mark)

(c) The process is carried out at a pressure of 200 atmospheres. If the pressure is increased, what effect will this have on the yield of this reaction?

.... (1 mark)

(d) An iron catalyst is used in the industrial production of ammonia. What effect does this catalyst have on

(i) the rate of this reaction

.... (1 mark)

(ii) the yield of this reaction

.... (1 mark)

Score   /6

How well did you do?
1–5   Try again
6–10   Getting there
11–13 Good work
14–18 Excellent!

TOTAL SCORE   /18

**For more on this topic
see page 78 of your Success Guide**

RELATIVE FORMULA MASS

A Choose just one answer, a, b, c or d.

1 The relative atomic mass of an element is the average mass of its isotopes compared with an atom of
(a) carbon-13   (c) hydrogen-1
(b) carbon-12   (d) oxygen-16   (1 mark)

2 The simplest ratio of atoms is called
(a) formula mass
(b) molecular formula
(c) empirical formula
(d) molecular mass   (1 mark)

3 What is the percentage composition of carbon in carbon dioxide, CO_2?
(a) 72%   (c) 0.27%
(b) 27%   (d) 33%   (1 mark)

4 What is the percentage of hydrogen in water, H_2O?
(a) 11%   (c) 66%
(b) 0.11%   (d) 50%   (1 mark)

5 What is the percentage of calcium in calcium carbonate, $CaCO_3$?
(a) 0.4%   (c) 0.6%
(b) 60%   (d) 40%   (1 mark)

Score   /5

B Answer all parts of the questions.

1 Calculate the relative formula mass of each of these molecules.

(a) carbon dioxide, CO_2 ....

(b) water, H_2O ....

(c) ammonia, NH_3 ....

(d) methane, CH_4 ....

(e) oxygen, O_2 ....

(f) nitrogen, N_2 ....   (6 marks)

2 Calculate the percentage composition of carbon in each of these compounds.

(a) carbon monoxide, CO ....

(b) methane, CH_4 ....

(c) ethene, C_2H_4 ....   (6 marks)

Score   /12

C

This is a GCSE-style question. Answer all parts of the question.

1 In his experiment a student reacted the metal magnesium with sulphuric acid. A diagram of his experiment is shown below.

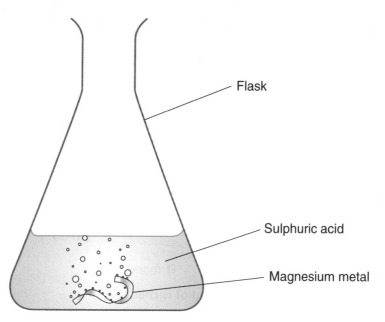

Flask

Sulphuric acid

Magnesium metal

(a) How could the student tell that a reaction had taken place?

.... (1 mark)

(b) One of the products made in this reaction is the salt, magnesium sulphate. Complete the equation below to show the other product that is made.

Magnesium + sulphuric acid ➔ magnesium sulphate + ... (1 mark)

(c) You may find the information in the table below useful when answering this question.

Element	Relative formula mass
magnesium	24
sulphur	32
oxygen	16
hydrogen	1

(i) Calculate the percentage of magnesium in magnesium sulphate, $MgSO_4$.

....

.... (2 marks)

(ii) Calculate the percentage of sulphur in magnesium sulphate, $MgSO_4$.

.... (1 mark)

Score   /5

How well did you do?

1–7   Try again
8–12   Getting there
13–18 Good work
19–22 Excellent!

TOTAL SCORE   /22

For more on this topic see page 80 of your Success Guide

RELATIVE FORMULA MASS 2

A

Choose just one answer, a, b, c or d.

1 What is the relative formula mass of carbon monoxide, CO?
(a) 44   (c) 2
(b) 28   (d) 20   (1 mark)

2 What is the relative formula mass of magnesium oxide, MgO?
(a) 40
(b) 80
(c) 20
(d) 100   (1 mark)

3 What is the percentage composition of carbon in carbon monoxide, CO?
(a) 41%
(b) 0.43%
(c) 43%
(d) 33%   (1 mark)

4 What is the percentage composition of oxygen in water, H_2O?
(a) 89%   (c) 0.89%
(b) 8.9%   (d) 33%   (1 mark)

5 What is the percentage of magnesium in magnesium carbonate, $MgCO_3$?
(a) 25%   (c) 0.29%
(b) 29%   (d) 75%   (1 mark)

Score /5

B

Answer all parts of the questions.

1 Calculate the relative formula mass of each of these molecules.

(a) hydrogen, H_2 ....

(b) chlorine, Cl_2 ....

(c) ethane, C_2H_6 ....

(d) ethene, C_2H_4 ....

(e) propene, C_3H_6 ....

(f) hydrogen chloride, HCl .... (6 marks)

2 Calculate the percentage composition of magnesium in each of these compounds.

(a) magnesium oxide, MgO ....

(b) magnesium chloride, $MgCl_2$ ....

(c) magnesium nitrate, $Mg(NO_3)_2$ .... (6 marks)

Score /12

78

C **This is a GCSE-style question. Answer all parts of the question.**

You may find the information in the table below useful when answering the following questions.

Element	Relative formula mass
xenon	131
oxygen	16
fluorine	19

1 A group of scientists have made a compound which contains the Noble gas, xenon. The compound consists of xenon and oxygen only. Analysis of the compound shows that it contains 0.65 g of xenon and 0.32 g of oxygen.

(a) Calculate the empirical formula of this compound.

....

....

.... (2 marks)

(b) Given that the relative formula mass of this compound is 195, give the molecular formula of this compound.

....

.... (1 mark)

A second group of scientists have also managed to make a compound which contains xenon. They know that this compound contains xenon and fluorine only. Analysis of the compound showed that it contains 53% xenon and 47% fluorine.

(c) Calculate the empirical formula of this compound.

....

.... (2 marks)

(d) Given that the relative formula mass of this compound is known to be 245, give the molecular formula of this compound.

....

.... (1 mark)

(e) Why are compounds of xenon not often made?

....

.... (1 mark)

Score   /7

How well did you do?

0–9   Try again
10–15 Getting there
16–19 Good work
20–24 Excellent!

TOTAL SCORE   /24

**For more on this topic
see pages 64–65 of your Success Guide**

BALANCING EQUATIONS

A

Choose just one answer, a, b, c or d.

1 What does the state symbol (s) show?
(a) salt
(b) strong
(c) liquid
(d) solid   (1 mark)

2 What does the state symbol (aq) show?
(a) dissolved in water
(b) it is water
(c) liquid
(d) solid   (1 mark)

3 How many oxygen atoms are present in one molecule of carbon dioxide, CO_2?
(a) 4
(b) 3
(c) 2
(d) 1   (1 mark)

4 How many carbon atoms are present in one molecule of octane, C_8H_{18}?
(a) 18   (c) 8
(b) 10   (d) 26   (1 mark)

5 How many atoms in total are present in one molecule of octane, C_8H_{18}?
(a) 18   (c) 8
(b) 10   (d) 26   (1 mark)

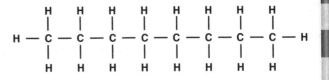

Score   /5

B

Answer all parts of the question.

1 Balance these equations.

(a) ....Na + ... Cl_2 → .... NaCl

(b) ....N_2 + ... H_2 → .... NH_3

(c) ....CH_4 + ...O_2 → ....CO_2 + ...H_2O

(d) ....C_2H_6 + ...O_2 → ....CO_2 + ...H_2O

(e) ....C + ...O_2 → ....CO

(f) ....C + ...CO_2 → ....CO

(g) ....Mg + ...O_2 → ....MgO

(h) ....H_2 + ...O_2 → ....H_2O

(i) ....H_2 + ...I_2 → ....HI

(j) ....H_2 + ...Cl_2 → ....HCl

(k) ....KI + ...Cl_2 → ....KCl + ...I_2

(l) ....Ca + ...O_2 → ....CaO

(m)..............H_2 + ...Br_2 → ....HBr

(n) ....K + ...I_2 → ....KI

(14 marks)

Score   /14

C **This is a GCSE-style question. Answer all parts of the question.**

1 Geologists are scientists who study rocks.
One common rock is called limestone. Limestone contains the mineral calcium carbonate, $CaCO_3$. Many geologists carry bottles of hydrochloric acid. If they think a rock may be limestone, they will test it by placing a couple of drops of hydrochloric acid on the rock. If the rock fizzes, the geologists know that the rock is limestone.

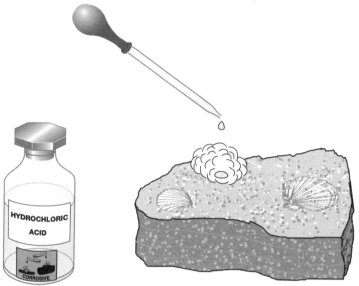

The reaction between calcium carbonate and hydrochloric acid can be represented by a word equation.

Calcium carbonate + hydrochloric acid ➜ calcium chloride + water + carbon dioxide

(a) Why does the limestone fizz when hydrochloric acid is dropped onto it?

.... (1 mark)

(b) Calcium carbonate can be represented by the formula $CaCO_3$.

   (i) How many atoms of calcium are represented by this formula?

   .... (1 mark)

   (ii) How many atoms of carbon are represented by this formula?

   .... (1 mark)

   (iii) How many different elements are represented by this formula?

   .... (1 mark)

(c) Balance the symbol equation below to show the reaction between calcium carbonate and hydrochloric acid

(1 mark)

   ....$CaCO_{3(s)}$ + ...$HCl_{(aq)}$ ➜ ....$CaCl_{2(aq)}$ + ...$H_2O_{(g)}$ + ...$CO_{2(g)}$

Score   /5

ow well did you do?
   1–5   Try again
   6–11 Getting there
   12–15 Good work
   16–24 Excellent!

TOTAL SCORE /24

For more on this topic see page 82 of your Success Guide

81

CALCULATING MASSES

A Choose just one answer, a, b, c or d.

1 If 24 g of magnesium is burnt, what mass of magnesium oxide, MgO is produced?
(a) 26 g (c) 20 g
(b) 40 g (d) 80 g   (1 mark)

2 If 12 g of magnesium is burnt, what mass of magnesium oxide, MgO is produced?
(a) 26 g (c) 20 g
(b) 40 g (d) 80 g   (1 mark)

3 If 80 g of calcium is burnt, what mass of calcium oxide, CaO, is produced?
(a) 96 g
(b) 112 g
(c) 160 g
(d) 80 g   (1 mark)

4 What volume will one mole of a gas occupy?
(a) 12 dm^3 (c) 96 dm^3
(b) 24 dm^3 (d) 48 dm^3 (1 mark)

5 What volume will 14 g of nitrogen, N$_2$, occupy?
(a) 12 dm^3 (c) 96 dm^3
(b) 24 dm^3 (d) 48 dm^3 (1 mark)

Score   /5

B Answer all parts of the questions.

1 Match the mass of each gas to the volume it will occupy.   (5 marks)

(a) 142 g of chlorine, Cl$_2$	24 dm^3
(b) 16 g of oxygen, O$_2$	12 dm^3
(c) 5 g of neon, Ne	48 dm^3
(d) 84 g of nitrogen, N$_2$	6 dm^3
(e) 2 g of hydrogen, H$_2$	72 dm^3

2 (a) What mass of magnesium should be used to make 100 g of magnesium oxide?

....
.... (2 marks)

(b) Hydrochloric acid reacts with magnesium to make magnesium chloride and hydrogen.

$2HCl_{(aq)} + Mg_{(s)} \rightarrow MgCl_{2(aq)} + H_{2(g)}$

What mass of magnesium should be used to make 4 g of hydrogen?

....
.... (2 marks)

Score   /9

This is a GCSE-style question. Answer all parts of the question.

1 Marble is a metamorphic rock. Marble contains the compound calcium carbonate.

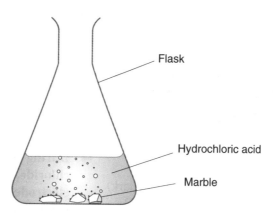

Flask

Hydrochloric acid

Marble

Calcium carbonate has the formula $CaCO_3$.

(a) Calculate the relative formula mass of calcium carbonate.

.... (1 mark)

(b) Calculate the percentage of calcium in calcium carbonate.

....

.... (2 marks)

(c) Marble reacts with hydrochloric acid.

The reaction can be represented by the equation

$$CaCO_{3(s)} + 2HCl_{(aq)} \rightarrow CaCl_{2(aq)} + H_2O_{(l)} + CO_{2(g)}$$

(i) Calculate the mass of carbon dioxide that would be produced when 5 g of calcium carbonate reacts fully with hydrochloric acid.

....

.... (2 marks)

(ii) Calculate the mass of calcium chloride that would be produced during the same reaction

....

.... (2 marks)

Score   /7

How well did you do?

1–5   Try again
6–11   Getting there
12–15 Good work
16–21 Excellent!

TOTAL SCORE   /21

For more on this topic
see page 84 of your Success Guide

ELECTROLYSIS

A

Choose just one answer, a, b, c or d.

1 What occurs during all REDOX reactions?
(a) the volume of gas stays the same
(b) reduction and oxidation
(c) reduction only
(d) oxidation only   (1 mark)

2 During electrolysis what happens at the positive electrode?
(a) electrons are lost
(b) electrons are gained
(c) metals are deposited
(d) sodium is deposited   (1 mark)

3 During electrolysis what happens at the negative electrode?
(a) electrons are lost
(b) electrons are gained

(c) gases are always made
(d) oxygen is always made   (1 mark)

4 During the electrolysis of molten sodium chloride, what is produced at the positive electrode?
(a) sodium metal   (c) hydrogen gas
(b) calcium metal   (d) chlorine gas   (1 mark)

5 During the electrolysis of molten sodium chloride, what is produced at the negative electrode?
(a) sodium metal
(b) calcium metal
(c) hydrogen gas
(d) chlorine gas   (1 mark)

Score   /5

B

Answer all parts of the questions.

1 The diagram below shows the electrolysis of molten potassium bromide, KBr. Use these names to label the diagram.

positive electrode

positive ion

bromine gas

negative electrode

negative ion

potassium metal

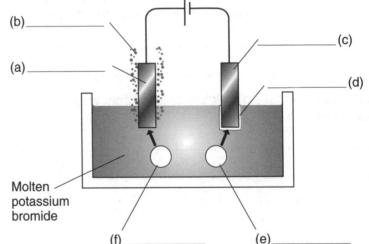

(b)_____

(a)_____

(c)

(d)

Molten
potassium
bromide

(f) _____   (e)_____   (6 marks)

2 During the electrolysis of molten potassium bromide, 1.56 g of potassium metal was deposited at the negative electrode.

(a) What mass of bromine, Br_2, was released at the positive electrode?

_____ (2 marks)

(b) What volume of bromine, Br_2, was released at the positive electrode?

_____ (2 marks)

Score   /10

C **This is a GCSE-style question. Answer all parts of the question.**

1 Molten lead bromide can be decomposed when it conducts electricity. This process is called electrolysis. A scientist carries out the experiment shown in the diagram below.

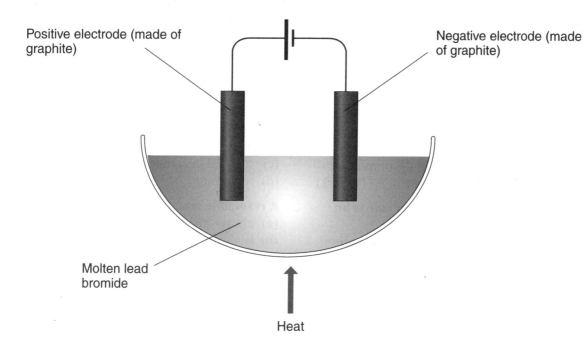

Positive electrode (made of graphite)

Negative electrode (made of graphite)

Molten lead bromide

Heat

Bromine vapour is produced at the positive electrode. The reaction at the positive electrode can be represented by a symbol equation.

$$2Br^-_{(l)} \rightarrow Br_{2(g)} + 2e^-$$

(a) Explain in words what happens at the positive electrode.

....

....

.... (3 marks)

Lead is produced at the negative electrode. The reaction at the negative electrode can be represented by a symbol equation.

(b) Balance the symbol equation below to show what happens at the negative electrode.

........$Pb^{2+}_{(l)}$ + ...$e^- \rightarrow$ ....$Pb_{(l)}$ (1 mark)

(c) Explain in words what happens at the negative electrode.

....

.... (2 marks)

Score   /6

How well did you do?

1–5   Try again
6–11   Getting there
12–15   Good work
16–21   Excellent!

TOTAL SCORE   /21

For more on this topic
see page 86 of your Success Guide

85

TYPES OF REACTION

A

Choose just one answer, a, b, c or d.

1 The reaction in which calcium carbonate is broken down into calcium oxide and carbon dioxide is an example of which type of reaction?
  (a) neutralisation (c) thermal decomposition
  (b) oxidation (d) reduction (1 mark)

2 The extraction of iron from iron oxide is an example of which type of reaction?
  (a) neutralisation (c) thermal decomposition
  (b) oxidation (d) reduction (1 mark)

3 The extraction of aluminium from aluminium oxide is an example of which type of reaction?
  (a) neutralisation (c) thermal decomposition
  (b) oxidation (d) reduction (1 mark)

4 The formation of copper oxide from copper is an example of which type of reaction?
  (a) neutralisation
  (b) oxidation
  (c) thermal decomposition
  (d) reduction (1 mark)

5 A reversible reaction:
  (a) always involves oxygen
  (b) is always exothermic
  (c) can proceed in either direction
  (d) is not useful (1 mark)

Score /5

B

Answer all parts of the question.

1 Harry has two beakers. One contains hydrochloric acid and the other contains sodium hydroxide. Harry measures the temperature of each solution, then mixes them together. He records the highest temperature that the new solution reaches.

Delete the incorrect word/s in the following phrases

This experiment is a neutralisation/reduction reaction.

Acids react with alkalis to form a salt and water/hydrogen.

Hydrochloric acid reacts with sodium hydroxide to form sodium sulphate/sodium chloride and water.

The temperature increases during the reaction. This shows that heat energy is taken in/given out.

Neutralisation reactions are endothermic/exothermic.

Score /5

C **This is a GCSE-style question. Answer all parts of the question.**

1 The diagram shows how a student carried out a reaction between calcium carbonate and hydrochloric acid.

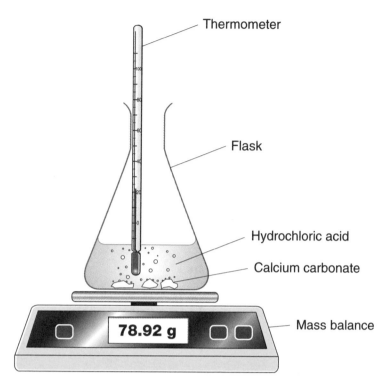

Thermometer

Flask

Hydrochloric acid

Calcium carbonate

78.92 g

Mass balance

(a) How could the student tell that a reaction had taken place?

.... (1 mark)

(b) What is the reaction between an acid and a base such as calcium carbonate called?

.... (1 mark)

(c) During this reaction, the student noticed that the temperature increased slightly. What is the name given to chemical reactions in which the temperature increases?

.... (1 mark)

(d) The student found that, during this reaction, calcium chloride, water and carbon dioxide were produced. Write a word equation to represent this reaction.

.... (1 mark)

(e) This reaction can also be represented using a symbol equation. Balance the symbol equation below to show this reaction. (1 mark)

........$CaCO_{3(s)}$ + ...$HCl_{(aq)}$ ➜ ....$CaCl_{2(aq)}$ + ...$CO_{2(g)}$ + ...$H_2O_{(l)}$

Score   /5

How well did you do?

1–5   Try again
6–9   Getting there
10–12 Good work
13–15 Excellent!

TOTAL SCORE   /15

For more on this topic
see page 88 of your Success Guide

MIXED GCSE-STYLE QUESTIONS

1 Consider the diagrams below.

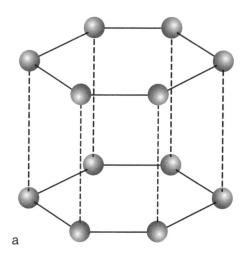

a

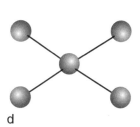

d

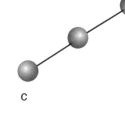

c

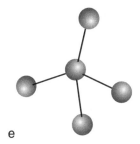

e

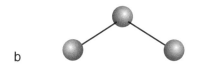

b

(a) Which of these diagrams best represents the structure of diamond?

.... (1 mark)

(b) Which of these diagrams best represents the structure of graphite?

.... (1 mark)

(c) Explain how the bonding in graphite means that carbon in the form of graphite is the only non-metal element that can conduct electricity.

....

....

....

....

.... (3 marks)

2 Methane is a hydrocarbon that is widely used as a fuel. The structural formula of a methane molecule is shown.

Draw a dots and crosses diagram to show how the electrons are arranged in a methane molecule.

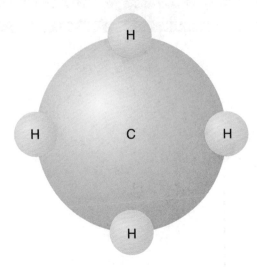

You may find this information useful.

Element	Proton number	Mass number
carbon	6	12
hydrogen	1	1

(2 marks)

3 Mineral water contains many dissolved salts. This means that mineral water contains many ions, the table below shows some of these ions.

Positive ions	mg* per litre	Negative ions	mg* per litre
calcium, Ca^{2+}	135	chloride, Cl^-	120
magnesium, Mg^{2+}	15	sulphate, SO_4^{2-}	15
potassium, K^+	5	nitrate, NO_3^-	25
sodium, Na^+	75		

*mg = milligram

(a) Name the Group I metal that is present in the highest concentration.

.... (1 mark)

(b) Name a metal from Group II of the periodic table.

.... (1 mark)

(c) Name the element from the third period of the periodic table that is present in the highest concentration.

.... (1 mark)

4 Nitrogen atoms combine with hydrogen atoms to make the compound ammonia. Each ammonia molecule consists of one nitrogen atom strongly bonded to three hydrogen atoms.

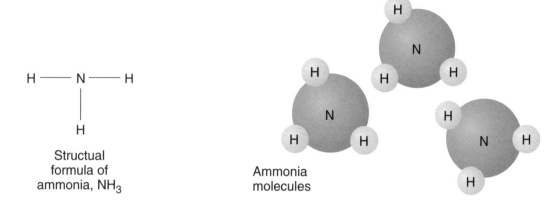

Structural formula of ammonia, NH_3

Ammonia molecules

(a) What type of bonding is present in the compound ammonia?

.... (1 mark)

(b) The boiling point of ammonia is −33°C. Explain in terms of the bonding involved why ammonia has a relatively low boiling point.

....

....

....

.... (2 marks)

5 The diagram shows how scientists believe that the Earth's continents looked 250 million years ago during the Permian period.

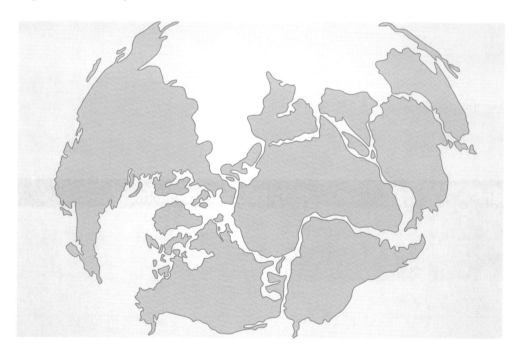

Scientists believe that the Earth's lithosphere is broken into a number of moving plates.

(a) What is the lithosphere?

....

.... (1 mark)

(b) Why do the plates move?

....

.... (1 mark)

(c) At what rate do the Earth's plates move?

....

.... (1 mark)

6 A student wants to make the salt, sodium sulphate. Which two substances should the student use? Choose two answers.

| sodium chloride | sodium hydroxide | hydrochloric acid | water | sulphuric acid |

.... (2 marks)

7 During the electrolysis of concentrated sodium chloride solution, the gas hydrogen is produced.

(a) Give one use of the gas hydrogen.

....

.... (1 mark)

(b) Two other useful chemicals are also produced during the electrolysis of sodium chloride solution. Which two substances are also made? Choose two answers.

| sodium | sodium hydroxide | hydrochloric acid | chlorine | oxygen |

....

.... (2 marks)

8 Calculate the percentage of calcium in calcium chloride, $CaCl_2$.

You may find the information in the table below useful.

Element	Relative atomic mass
calcium	40
chlorine	35.5

....

.... (2 marks)

9 Water vapour is produced when the gas hydrogen is burnt in air.

This reaction can be represented by the symbol equation

$$2H_{2(g)} + O_{2(g)} \rightarrow 2H_2O_{(g)}$$

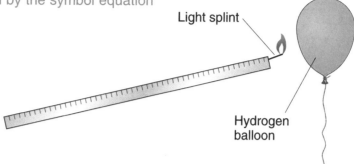

Light splint

Hydrogen balloon

Calculate the volume of water vapour which would be produced, if 8 g of hydrogen is burnt in plenty of oxygen.

....

....

.... (2 marks)

10 A student wants to make the salt potassium nitrate. Which two substances should the student use? Choose two answers.

| water | hydrochloric acid | potassium hydroxide | potassium chloride | nitric acid |

.... (2 marks)

11 A student wants to investigate the rate of reaction between the metal magnesium and sulphuric acid. The reaction can be represented by the word equation

Magnesium + sulphuric acid → magnesium sulphate + hydrogen

The diagram shows how the student carried out the experiment.

Flask

Magnesium

Sulphuric acid

Mass balance

(a) To calculate the rate of this reaction from the start to the finish, what measurements should the student take?

....

....
(2 marks)

(b) Calculate the percentage of magnesium in magnesium sulphate, $MgSO_4$. You may find the information in the table below useful.

Element	Relative atomic mass
magnesium, Mg	24
sulphur, S	32
oxygen, O	16

.... (2 marks)

12 **(a)** Name the gas, found in polluted areas, which causes acid rain.

.... (1 mark)

(b) Give one effect of acid rain.

....

.... (1 mark)

(c) Name a gas associated with global warming.

.... (1 mark)

(d) Give one possible effect of global warming.

....

.... (1 mark)

13 The table below shows the melting points and boiling points of four elements.

Element	Melting point (°C)	Boiling point °C
silicon	1410	2355
mercury	−39	357
radon	−71	−62
indium	156	2080

(a) Which of the elements shown in the table is a gas at room temperature?

.... (1 mark)

(b) Which of the elements shown in the table is a liquid at room temperature?

.... (1 mark)

14 The structural formula of a hydrocarbon is shown below.

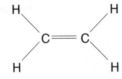

(a) Is this hydrocarbon an alkane or an alkene?

....

.... (1 mark)

(b) What is the name of this hydrocarbon?

....

.... (1 mark)

(c) Explain how you could test an unknown hydrocarbon to find out whether it is an alkane or an alkene.

....

....

.... (2 marks)

ANSWERS

1 **(a)** e

(b) a

(c) Each carbon atom is bonded to three other carbon atoms in the same layer by strong covalent bonds.
But the bonding between layers is much weaker. The electrons in these weak bonds can move and so graphite can conduct electricity.

2

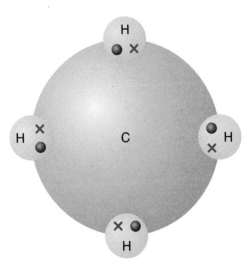

3 **(a)** sodium

(b) magnesium or calcium

(c) chlorine

4 **(a)** covalent

(b) There is strong bonding within each ammonia molecule, but only weak forces of attraction between ammonia molecules.

5 **(a)** crust and upper mantle

(b) Convection currents in the mantle.

(c) A few cm per year.

6 sodium hydroxide and sulphuric acid

7 **(a)** manufacture of margarine

(b) sodium hydroxide and chlorine

8 $40/111 \times 100 = 36\%$

9 $96 \ dm^3$

10 potassium hydroxide and nitric acid

11 **(a)** the mass of hydrogen made/given off, every minute/second, etc.

(b) $24/120 \times 100 = 20\%$

12 **(a)** sulphur dioxide

(b) damage to trees/lakes /buildings / statues

(c) carbon dioxide/methane

(d) disruption to normal weather patterns/flooding

13 **(a)** radon

(b) mercury

14 **(a)** alkene

(b) ethene

(c) Add bromine water.
alkene, decolourises /orange/brown to colourless